GCSE English

Frankenstein

by Mary Shelley

Analysing *Frankenstein* for GCSE English can seem like a monster challenge, but this CGP Workbook will help you bring your answers to life...

It's jam-packed with questions on the novel's plot, characters, themes, context and techniques... and it gets better! We've also included a whole section on writing great essays that will knock the examiner's socks off.

So don't be tempted to experiment with other *Frankenstein* Workbooks — with CGP, you'll be the real Victor in the exams!

The Workbook

CONTENTS

CONTENTS

Section Four — The Writer's Techniques

Section Five — Exam Buster

Published by CGP

Editors:
Claire Boulter
Tom Carney
Emma Cleasby
Kathryn Kaiser
Louise McEvoy

With thanks to Graham Fletcher and Matt Topping for the proofreading.
With thanks to Ana Pungartnik for the copyright research.

Acknowledgements:

Cover Illustration by Ricardo Sandoval

With thanks to Rex Features for permission to use the images on pages 1, 3, 4, 11, 16, 17, 19, 21, 23, 28, 30, 32, 35, and 38.

With thanks to ArenaPAL for permission to use the images on pages 7, 9, 12, 18, 20, 22, 27, 36.

ISBN: 978 1 78908 140 4

Printed by Elanders Ltd, Newcastle upon Tyne.

Clipart from Corel®

Based on the classic CGP style created by Richard Parsons.

Text, design, layout and original illustrations © Coordination Group Publications Ltd. (CGP) 2018

How to Use this Book

Practise the four main skills you'll need for the exam

Each question tests <u>one or more</u> of the <u>four skills</u> you'll be tested on in the <u>exam</u>. You'll need to:

1) Write about the text in a <u>thoughtful way</u>, <u>picking out</u> appropriate <u>examples</u> and <u>quotations</u> to back up your opinions.

2) <u>Identify</u> and <u>explain</u> features of the book's <u>form</u>, <u>structure</u> and <u>language</u>. Using <u>subject terminology</u>, show how the author uses these to create <u>characters</u> and <u>settings</u>, explore <u>themes</u> and affect the <u>reader's reactions</u>.

3) Write about the novel's <u>context</u> in your exam.

4) Write in a <u>clear</u>, <u>well-structured</u> and <u>accurate</u> way. <u>5%</u> of the marks in your English Literature GCSE are for <u>spelling</u>, <u>punctuation</u> and <u>grammar</u>.

Most exam boards will want you write about context. Ask your teacher if you're not sure.

You can use this workbook with the CGP Text Guide

1) This workbook is perfect to use with CGP's <u>Text Guide</u> for *Frankenstein*. It matches each <u>main section</u> of the Text Guide, so you can test your knowledge <u>bit by bit</u>.

2) The workbook covers all the <u>important</u> parts of the text that you'll need to know about for the exam — <u>plot</u>, <u>characters</u>, <u>context</u>, <u>themes</u> and the <u>writer's techniques</u>.

3) The questions refer to the text <u>in detail</u> — you'll need a <u>copy</u> of the novel to make the most of the workbook.

© Alastair Muir/REX/Shutterstock

It prepares you for the exam every step of the way

1) The exam section is crammed with <u>useful advice</u>. It <u>guides</u> you through how to tackle the exam, from understanding the questions to building great answers. There's also an easy-to-read <u>mark scheme</u>, which you can use to mark <u>sample answers</u> and improve answers of your <u>own</u>.

2) There are four pages of <u>practice exam questions</u> spread across the book. They give you the opportunity to use what you've revised in each section to write a <u>realistic answer</u>.

3) <u>Exam tips</u> and extra <u>practice exam questions</u> are included throughout the book. There are also helpful <u>revision tasks</u> designed to get you thinking more creatively. These are marked with <u>stamps</u>.

4) You can find <u>answers</u> to all of the <u>questions</u> and <u>tasks</u> at the back of the book.

5) Each section contains at least one '<u>Skills Focus</u>' page. These pages help you to practise important skills <u>individually</u>. You can tackle them in <u>any order</u> and prioritise the skills you find the <u>hardest</u>.

If this book doesn't animate your revision, nothing will...

Now you know what the book's all about, it's time to tackle some questions. Remember, you don't have to do the sections in order — use the book in a way that works for you. Just don't sneak a look at the answers first...

2

Section One — Analysis of Chapters

Walton's Letters

Walton rescues Frankenstein in the Arctic

Q1 Read Letter 1 from "**I am already far north of London**" to "**embark in a seafaring life**". Where does Walton plan to go on his voyage?

....

Q2 Decide whether each statement is **true** or **false**, and find a quote to back up your answer.

a) In Letter 2, Shelley shows that Walton is fond of his sister. **True:** ☐ **False:** ☐

Quote: ....

b) In Letter 4, Frankenstein seems ungrateful about being rescued. **True:** ☐ **False:** ☐

Quote: ....

Q3 Read Letter 4 from "**About two o'clock**" to "**rest for a few hours**". How does Shelley make the Arctic seem dangerous in this extract? Support your answer using a quote from the text.

....

....

....

Q4 Put these events in order by numbering the boxes.
The first one has been done for you.

Frankenstein warns Walton about the dangers of ambition. ☐

A large creature is spotted travelling across the ice on a dog sled. ☐

Frankenstein explains that he is trying to track someone down. ☐

Walton's ship gets stuck in the frozen sea of the Arctic. ☐ 1

Frankenstein offers to tell Walton his story as a warning. ☐

A stranger is discovered close to death on the ice and is brought aboard. ☐

Reaching the North Pole? Seems like child's play...

It may seem like not much happens in the letters, but they introduce many of the novel's key themes and give the reader an impression of Frankenstein's character, so it's important to know them well.

Section One — Analysis of Chapters

Chapters 1 and 2

Frankenstein begins his story

Q1 According to Frankenstein, why did his father show so much love towards Caroline?

....

Q2 Why do you think Caroline decided to adopt Elizabeth?

....

Q3 Explain the impact that Elizabeth had on the characters below during their childhoods. Give a quote from Chapter 2 to support each answer.

a) Frankenstein: ....

Quote: ....

b) Clerval: ....

Quote: ....

Q4 What is it about science that fascinates Frankenstein so much in Chapter 2? Support your answer using a quote from the text.

....

....

....

© SNAP/REX/Shutterstock

Q5 Read Chapter 2 from "**Thus strangely are our souls constructed**" to the end of the chapter. How does this chapter ending create suspense for the reader?

....

....

....

Frankenstein gets Agrippa on his scientific education...

Look back at Walton's description of his childhood in Letters 1 and 2, and compare it to Frankenstein's in Chapters 1 and 2. Make a table comparing the similarities and differences between their youths.

Section One — Analysis of Chapters

Chapters 3 to 5

Frankenstein makes the monster

Q1 Put these events in order by numbering the boxes.
The first one has been done for you.

Frankenstein discovers the secret of creating life. ☐

Frankenstein's mother dies of scarlet fever. 1

Clerval nurses Frankenstein back to health. ☐

Frankenstein builds a monster out of human remains. ☐

Frankenstein begins his studies at the university of Ingolstadt. ☐

Frankenstein falls very ill. ☐

Q2 Find a quote from Chapter 3 to back up each of these statements.

a) Frankenstein feels like his life is not under his control.

....

b) Waldman sees the value of Frankenstein's previous studies.

....

....

Q3 Read Chapter 4 from "**These thoughts supported**" to "**I brought my work near to a conclusion**". Describe Frankenstein's mental state in this extract.

....

....

Q4 Why do you think Frankenstein reacts so negatively to the monster in Chapter 5? Explain your answer.

....

....

....

Ignore it all you like Victor, the monster's here to stay...

...unsurprising, given he's built out of remains. If only Frankenstein's enthusiasm for the monster had stayed too — write a paragraph summarising the events that lead Frankenstein to create the monster.

Chapters 6 to 8

The monster kills Frankenstein's brother

Q1 Find a quote from Chapter 6 to back up each of these statements.

a) Frankenstein is grateful for Clerval's friendship.

....

b) Nature helps Frankenstein to feel happy again.

....

Q2 What causes the mood of the novel get darker at the start of Chapter 7?

....

Q3 Read Chapter 7 from "**It was completely dark**" to "**the east of the lake**". How is the weather used to create tension in this extract? Use a quote to support your answer.

....

....

....

Q4 Answer each question below, then choose a quote from Chapter 8 to support your answers.

a) Why does Justine confess to William's murder even though she is innocent?

....

Quote: ....

b) Why does Frankenstein feel so guilty at the end of the chapter?

....

Quote: ....

William Frankenstein's death is ~~throat-~~ heart-wrenching...

It takes two innocent deaths for Frankenstein to start to realise the consequences of his decision to create life. Think about other times in the novel when Frankenstein realises things too little, too late.

Chapters 9 and 10

Frankenstein finally meets the monster

Q1 Frankenstein says he "**shunned the face of man**" in Chapter 9. Explain what this suggests about how Frankenstein feels about himself at this point in the novel.

....

....

Q2 Read Chapter 10 from "**The ascent is precipitous**" to "**may convey to us**". How does Shelley create a bleak setting in this extract? Explain your answer.

....

....

....

Q3 Decide whether each statement is **true** or **false**, and find a quote to back up your answer.

a) Frankenstein is pleased to see the monster.   True: ☐   False: ☐

Quote: ....

b) The monster is surprised at Frankenstein's response to him.   True: ☐   False: ☐

Quote: ....

c) Frankenstein eventually agrees to hear the monster's story.   True: ☐   False: ☐

Quote: ....

Q4 How might the reader's impression of the monster change after he begins to speak? Support your answer with a quote.

....

....

....

Mountain air to soothe a weary soul — every little Alps...
The mood in Chapters 9 and 10 changes from despair to joy and then back again. Write a short paragraph explaining why you think Shelley chose to create contrasting moods in these chapters.

Section One — Analysis of Chapters

Chapters 11 and 12

The monster tells Frankenstein about his early life

Q1 Why do you think Shelley chooses to include the monster's
first moments at the start of his narration in Chapter 11?

....

....

....

© Johan Persson / ArenaPAL

Q2 Decide whether each statement is **true** or **false**, and find a quote to back up your answer.

a) The monster is overwhelmed by his surroundings at first.   **True:** ☐   **False:** ☐

Quote: ....

b) The monster isn't interested in the houses he discovers.   **True:** ☐   **False:** ☐

Quote: ....

Q3 Find a quote to back up each of these statements.

Statement	Quote that shows this
a) The monster learns basic survival skills.	
b) The monster tries to help the De Laceys.	
c) The monster is repulsed by his own appearance.	

Q4 What is it about the De Laceys' behaviour that appeals
to the monster? Use a quote to support your answer.

....

....

Chapters 13 and 14

The monster explains how he learned to speak and read

Q1 Find a quote from Chapter 13 to back up each of these statements.

a) The monster is quick to learn the De Laceys' language.

....

b) The monster begins to understand that society can be cruel.

....

Q2 Read Chapter 13 from "**The words induced**" to "**Miserable, unhappy wretch!**"
In your own words, summarise the monster's thoughts about himself in this extract.

....

....

....

Q3 At the end of Chapter 13, the monster refers to his "**innocent, half-painful self-deceit**". What is the 'self-deceit' that he is referring to?

....

....

Q4 Fill in the paragraph below about Chapter 14 using the correct words from the box.

The De Laceys' history is the first example of .... human ....

that the monster experiences. Felix .... helps an outsider in society to escape

.... despite the risk to himself. Then, after his family are ....

because of his actions, Felix turns himself in to the .... in the hope that his family

will be released. This emphasises the .... that the De Laceys have for each other.

> imprisoned   cruel   injustice   behaviour   authorities   kind   love   killed   selflessly   unwillingly

A is for Agatha, B is for Book, C is for Can't stop revising...

Make notes comparing Frankenstein's relationship with knowledge in Chapter 2 to the monster's relationship with it here. Then decide if knowledge has been presented positively or negatively so far.

Chapters 15 and 16

It all goes wrong for the monster

Q1 Why does *Paradise Lost* have such a strong impact on the monster?

....

Q2 'Felix's reaction to the monster is unexpected.' Do you agree? Explain your answer.

....

....

Q3 Put these events from Chapter 16 in order by numbering the boxes. The first one has been done for you.

The monster learns that William is related to Frankenstein and kills him. ☐

The monster recovers from his injury and reaches Geneva. ☐

The monster meets William and attempts to befriend him, but he is rejected. ☐

The De Laceys flee their home, and the monster sets fire to it in rage. ☐ 1

The monster frames Justine for William's murder. ☐

Q4 Read Chapter 16 from "**When night came**" to "**enjoyed the ruin**". How does Shelley use language in this extract to suggest that the monster is becoming less human?

....

....

....

Q5 Why does the monster frame Justine? Use a quote to support your answer.

....

....

....

....

© Nigel Norrington / ArenaPAL

 ☐   ☐   ☐

Chapters 17 to 20

Frankenstein starts a female monster then destroys it

Q1 Decide whether each statement is **true** or **false**, and find a quote to back up your answer.

    a) Frankenstein thinks that the monster is completely unreasonable.   **True:** ☐   **False:** ☐

    Quote: ....

    b) In Chapter 18, Shelley suggests that Frankenstein wants to be alone.   **True:** ☐   **False:** ☐

    Quote: ....

Q2 Look back at Chapter 19. In your own words, summarise
how Frankenstein feels about making a second monster.

....

....

Q3 Read Chapter 20 from "**'You have destroyed**" to "**injuries you inflict'**". What impression do
you get of the relationship between Frankenstein and the monster at this point in the novel?

....

....

....

Q4 What does Frankenstein do when the monster threatens to be with him on his wedding night?

....

Q5 Read Chapter 20 from "**As I was occupied**" to the end of the chapter.
Find a quote from this extract that creates a tense atmosphere and explain how it does this.

    Quote: ....

    Explanation: ....

....

Packing checklist: coat, socks, hat, dead body parts...

This is the second time Frankenstein attempts to make a monster, but his motivations are different here.
He's now motivated by a sense of fear and duty. Think about how this change affects the novel's mood.

    ☐   ☐   ☐

Chapters 21 and 22

Clerval is murdered, and Frankenstein marries Elizabeth

Q1 Give two reasons why Frankenstein is suspected of Clerval's murder.

1) ....

2) ....

Q2 Why is Frankenstein horrified when Kirwin tells him "**someone, a friend, is come to visit you**"?

....

Q3 In Chapter 21, Alphonse comes to take Frankenstein home. Explain what effect Alphonse's arrival has on Frankenstein's state of mind. Use a quote to support your answer.

....

....

Q4 Find a quote from Chapter 22 to back up each of these statements.

a) Alphonse suspects that Frankenstein doesn't want to marry Elizabeth.

....

b) Elizabeth ignores her fears about her future with Frankenstein.

....

Q5 Read Chapter 22 from "**Great God! If for one instant**" to "**everlasting regret**". How does Shelley create a threatening mood in this extract?

....

....

....

....

© McPix Ltd/REX/Shutterstock

EXAM TIP

Victor will make a fine husband — why, he's to die for...

Pay attention to the mood in Chapter 22 — the wedding should be a happy occasion, but both Victor and Elizabeth are apprehensive about it. This hints at the dreadful event to come in the next chapter.

Chapters 23 and 24

The monster kills Elizabeth and Frankenstein vows revenge

Q1 How does Shelley make Elizabeth's murder shocking for the reader? Explain your answer.

....

....

....

Q2 How does Frankenstein misinterpret the monster's threat about his wedding night?

....

....

Q3 What causes Alphonse's death?

....

Q4 Find a quote from Chapter 24 to back up each of these statements.

a) Frankenstein believes that his quest for revenge is guided by something supernatural.

....

b) The monster does not want Frankenstein to die on their journey to the Arctic.

....

Q5 Why do you think Shelley chooses to highlight similarities between Frankenstein and the monster in Chapters 23 and 24?

....

....

....

....

MAKING LINKS

An eye for an eye, a wife for a lady-monster...

Frankenstein uses very passionate language when he's vowing his revenge. Think about other points in the novel where characters use passionate language and what has driven them to such extremes.

'Walton, in continuation'

Frankenstein dies and the monster promises to kill himself

Q1 Walton appreciates Frankenstein's presence on the ship. Give an example of Frankenstein helping Walton in this part of the novel.

....

....

Q2 Read from "**When younger**" to "**never again to rise**". How does Frankenstein justify his creation of the monster? Use a quote to support your answer.

....

....

....

Q3 Decide whether each statement is **true** or **false**, and find a quote to back up your answer.

a) Walton is forced to give up on his dream of exploring the Arctic. **True:** ☐ **False:** ☐

Quote: ....

....

b) The monster is proud of his role in Frankenstein's death. **True:** ☐ **False:** ☐

Quote: ....

....

Q4 To what extent do you think Frankenstein blames himself for his mistakes by the time he dies? Explain your answer.

....

....

....

To be frank(enstein), he got what he deserved...

Look back over the novel and make a flowchart showing the main events that lead to Frankenstein's death. You should include at least five key events and use arrows to show the links between them.

 ☐   ☐   ☐

Using Quotes

There's no point in having lots of really good opinions about the book if you can't back them up with evidence — that's where quotes from the text come in. You won't have the book with you in the exam, so you'll need to choose some useful quotes to learn beforehand. Picking quotes isn't always easy, so here's a page to help you think about the sort of quotes you might learn and how to use them successfully in your answers. Have a go at these questions and you'll soon have cracked it.

Q1 Complete the table below to show whether each way of using quotes is good or bad. Put a tick in the relevant column.

Way of using quotes	Good	Bad
a) Writing down quotes exactly as they're written in the text		
b) Using quotes that repeat exactly what you've just written		
c) Using quotes as part of your sentence, rather than adding them onto the end of it		
d) Including lots of long quotes		
e) Using quotes which are interesting but don't back up your point		

Q2 Look at the examples and decide which use quotes well and which use them badly.

a) Frankenstein thinks that it would be morally wrong to leave his family so soon after his mother's death, describing it as "sacrilege" to "rush" into his new life at university.

b) The monster learns that De Lacey "was descended from a good family in France, where he had lived for many years in affluence, respected by his superiors and beloved by his equals."

c) The novel ends mysteriously, as the monster is "lost in darkness" and his fate is uncertain.

d) The monster angrily curses his creator when he calls Frankenstein a "Cursed, cursed creator!"

e) 'Romantic' ideas are explored in Chapter 9 when Frankenstein describes how the "scene of singular beauty" on his journey to the valley of Chamounix lifted his spirits.

Good Quote Usage: ....   Bad Quote Usage: ....

Q3 Choose one of the examples you identified as bad in Q2 and improve it.

....

....

....

P.E.E.D.

Making a comment about the book is all well and good, but if you want a good mark, you'll need to explain your comment in a clear and developed way. The trick is to stick to the P.E.E.D. method. Whenever you make a **point**, back it up with an **example**, then **explain** how it supports your point. The last step is to **develop** your point by explaining the effect it has on the reader or by linking it to something else. This could be another part of the book, a theme, or a relevant piece of context.

Q1 None of the sample answers below have used P.E.E.D. correctly. For each, say which stage of P.E.E.D. is missing, then write a sentence you could include to improve the answer.

a)

> The monster's loneliness is presented as unbearable. He envies Satan who had "companions, fellow devils", whereas he is "solitary". This reference to Satan emphasises how miserable loneliness makes him by implying he thinks life in Hell would be better than the life he is living.

Missing Stage: .... Addition: ....

....

....

b)

> Frankenstein's mental state deteriorates under the increasing amount of strain he faces until, in Ireland, his life appears "as a dream" and he doubts "if indeed it were all true". By the end of the novel, Frankenstein's hold on reality has lessened even more and he begs unseen "spirits" to help him in his quest for revenge.

Missing Stage: .... Addition: ....

....

....

c)

> Shelley presents Caroline as a selfless character. This emphasises her benevolent nature by showing how she risks her own life to care for her family. Her selfless sacrifice makes Frankenstein's desertion of the monster seem more shocking and selfish.

Missing Stage: .... Addition: ....

....

....

Section One — Analysis of Chapters

Section Two — Characters

Victor Frankenstein

Q1 Look at these statements about Frankenstein.
Decide which are **true** and which are **false**.

	True	False
Frankenstein had a happy childhood.	☐	☐
He sometimes displays addictive behaviour.	☐	☐
He manages to keep careful control of his emotions.	☐	☐
Frankenstein never realises how destructive his ambition has been.	☐	☐
He is eager to tell other people about his method for creating life.	☐	☐

Q2 Read Letter 4 from "**Upon hearing this**" to "**restored him wonderfully**".
Find a quote which shows how Frankenstein's pursuit of the monster
has affected him. What effect does this portrayal have on the reader?

Quote: ....

Effect: ....

Q3 Read from the start of Chapter 8 to "**her who suffered through me**".
Explain what impression the reader gets of Frankenstein in this extract.

....

....

....

....

© SNAP/REX/Shutterstock

Q4 Explain one way in which you think Frankenstein's abandonment of the monster
when it wakes up is unforgivable **and** one way in which it is forgiveable.

Unforgivable: ....

....

Forgivable: ....

....

A Victor who loses everything — pretty ironic...

Read Chapter 4 from "**When I found so astonishing**" to "**devoted the body to corruption**", then plan
an answer to the following question: **How far are Frankenstein's motivations for creating the monster
presented as selfish?** In your plan, you should refer to both the extract and the novel as whole.

 ☐   ☐   ☐

The Monster

Q1 The monster is called many things by other characters in the novel. Read the different descriptions below and explain what each one suggests about how the monster is viewed.

What characters call him	What it suggests
a) Victor Frankenstein: "**creature**"	
b) William Frankenstein: "**ogre**"	
c) Robert Walton: "**fiend**"	

Q2 Read Chapter 12 from "**A considerable period elapsed**" to "**cultivating the garden**". Explain how Shelley shows the monster's natural desire to do good in this passage.

....

....

....

Q3 Find a quote from Chapter 15 to back up each of these statements.

a) The monster is curious about the world.

....

b) The monster longs for company and affection.

....

© Moviestore Collection/REX/Shutterstock

Q4 Read the part of Chapter 10 where Frankenstein and the monster meet for the first time. Explain how the monster feels about Frankenstein. Use a quote to support your answer.

....

....

....

What's the monster's dream dinner? Franken-furters...

EXAM TIP

The monster is a complicated character, so don't be afraid to discuss him sympathetically. Showing you understand why he does evil things will give your answers more depth and impress the examiner.

Section Two — Characters

Robert Walton

Q1 Find a quote from Letter 1 to back up each of these statements.

a) Walton is optimistic about his expedition.

....

b) He dreams of greatness.

....

c) He worked hard to prepare himself for life at sea.

....

Q2 Read from "**I cannot describe to you**" to the end of Letter 2. How does Walton's language convey his feelings about the coming voyage to the reader? Use a quote to support your answer.

....

....

....

....

Q3 Look at these statements about Walton.
Decide which are **true** and which are **false**.

	True	False
Walton regrets that he is not better educated.	☐	☐
He admires Frankenstein.	☐	☐
Walton feels responsible for the lives of his crew.	☐	☐
His first reaction to the monster is one of pity.	☐	☐

© Johan Persson / ArenaPAL

Q4 Explain what Walton choosing to return home shows about his character. Use a quote to support your answer.

....

....

....

Rob the explorer — a highwayman's favourite pastime...

MAKING LINKS

Walton's letters to Margaret show the reader he cares about her and link him to the theme of family in the novel. Think about other times that letters are used to show affection in *Frankenstein*.

Henry Clerval

Q1 Clerval is linked to **"books of chivalry and romance"** in Chapter 2. What does this tell the reader about his character? Give reasons for your answer.

© ITV/REX/Shutterstock

....

....

....

Q2 Find an example from the novel which shows that Clerval is close to the Frankenstein family.

....

Q3 Fill in the gaps in the table below. The first one has been done for you.

Action in the novel	What it suggests about Clerval
a) Clerval gives up studying to nurse Frankenstein back to health in Ingolstadt.	He is a loving, caring and selfless friend.
b) Clerval is moved by the natural beauty of Switzerland and Germany.	
c) Clerval wants to learn from intelligent and talented people in London.	

Q4 Clerval is always presented positively. How does this affect the reader's reaction to his death?

....

....

....

Q5 Explain how Clerval plays an important role in the novel.

....

....

....

PRACTICE TASK

Nice guys finish, er, dead?...

Poor Henry. He didn't deserve to die, but monsters just don't care about fairness. List three times when Clerval has a positive effect on Frankenstein. For each one, explain how this effect is achieved.

Elizabeth Lavenza

Q1 Give two examples of events in the novel which show that Elizabeth is emotionally strong.

1) ....

2) ....

Q2 Fill in the gaps in the table below. The first one has been done for you.

Description of Elizabeth	What the imagery suggests about Elizabeth
a) "Her hair... seemed to set a crown of distinction on her head".	Describing Elizabeth's hair as a "**crown**" implies that she is noble. The noun "**distinction**" suggests that she is superior to other people.
b) "The saintly soul of Elizabeth shone like a shrine-dedicated lamp"	
c) "She indeed veiled her grief"	

Q3 Why do you think Shelley mentions Elizabeth so frequently in the novel? Use a quote to support your answer.

....

....

....

....

© JONES Pete/ArenaPAL/ ArenaPAL

Q4 Caroline presents Elizabeth as a "**gift**" to Frankenstein, who calls her "**mine**". What does this suggest about Elizabeth?

....

....

....

Frankenstein's Parents

Q1 Look at these statements about Alphonse and Caroline Frankenstein.
Decide which are **true** and which are **false**.

	True	False
Alphonse is a loyal and devoted friend.	☐	☐
Caroline is a selfless person.	☐	☐
Caroline asked Elizabeth's biological parents for permission to adopt her.	☐	☐
Alphonse encourages Victor to read about natural philosophy.	☐	☐

Q2 Find a quote which shows Caroline behaving kindly and explain how it does this.

Quote: ....

Explanation: ....

....

Q3 Fill in the paragraph below by using the right words from the box.

As a syndic, or a .... official, Alphonse believes in justice and the law. These

beliefs come into .... with his other loyalties in the novel. For example, he is

caught between his faith in the law and his family's belief that Justine is .... in

Chapter 7. When Frankenstein is .... for Clerval's murder, Alphonse knows he is

innocent, which suggests he has learnt that .... doesn't always treat others fairly.

released innocent military arrested society battle government guilty conflict

Q4 Do you think that Alphonse and Caroline are good
parents? Use a quote to support your answer.

© ITV/REX/Shutterstock

....

....

....

These poor parents. Their grandson is a literal monster...

Read Chapter 1 from "**From Italy**" to "**guardian angel to the afflicted**". **How are attitudes towards
responsibility presented by Shelley here and elsewhere in the novel?** You should write about:

- what attitudes characters have towards responsibility
- how characters' attitudes to responsibility influence their behaviour.

  ☺ ☐

William and Justine

Q1 Look at these statements about William Frankenstein.
Decide which are **true** and which are **false**.

	True	False
William's presence brings his family great joy.	☐	☐
He views the monster with childlike innocence instead of horror.	☐	☐
William is presented as gentle and sweet-natured.	☐	☐
He is unpopular with other young children.	☐	☐

Q2 Find a quote from the novel which shows that
Justine is brave, then briefly explain how it does this.

Quote: ....

....

Explanation: ....

....

....

© Nigel Norrington / ArenaPAL

Q3 Read the two sentences below. Explain how each
one makes Justine's execution seem especially unjust.

a) Justine **"passed several hours"** looking for William on the night that he went missing.

....

b) Justine is **"threatened and menaced"** by a priest until she confesses her guilt.

....

Q4 Explain how William's and Justine's deaths affect Frankenstein's relationship with the monster.

....

....

....

PRACTICE TASK

Will's masseur is great — his neck work is to die for...

Have a think about why Shelley presents these two ~~victims~~ characters so virtuously before they die.
Write a paragraph for both William and Justine explaining how their goodness affects the reader.

Section Two — Characters

The De Laceys and Safie

Q1 Fill in the gaps in the table below to show what each quote suggests about the character who is being described. The first one has been done for you.

Character	Quote	What does the quote suggest?
a) De Lacey	"**The old man, I could perceive, often endeavoured to encourage his children**"	De Lacey tries to keep his children in good spirits, which shows that he's kind.
b) Felix	"**Felix carried with pleasure to his sister the first little white flower that peeped out**"	
c) Agatha	"**her eyes sometimes filled with tears, which she endeavoured to wipe away unperceived**"	

Q2 What do Felix's actions at the end of Chapter 15 show the reader about his character?

....

....

Q3 Fill in the paragraph below by using the right words from the box.

Safie and her father are victims of .... in the novel. Her father is punished more

severely for a crime because he follows another .... to those around him. This

demonstrates how .... is flawed by showing how badly it treats people that are

.... The De Laceys' .... of Safie suggests that they're good

people, but their .... of the monster reveals that even they judge him unfairly.

society   acceptance   prejudice   rejection   faithful   different   imperfect   hate   religion

Q4 Explain how De Lacey's blindness links to the theme of prejudice.

....

....

....

© ITV/REX/Shutterstock

Felix has a sweet tooth — he loves a Turkish delight...

Knowledge is linked to danger in the novel — it's to be treated with caution. The monster learns how alone he is during his time with the De Laceys, which makes him sad, mad and just a tad murder-y.

Making Links

A great way to develop your answer is to make links between the points you've made and other parts of the text. You could write about similar events, other times characters behave in the same way or other places where a theme is presented. This page will get you thinking about how some of the main characters behave in similar ways in different parts of the novel. Try to use specific examples from the text — this will help you to develop clear links between different parts of the novel.

Q1 Read the statements below, then answer each question.

a) In Chapter 12, De Lacey talks to Agatha to cheer her up.
Find an example of a character who behaves in a similar way in Chapter 21.

Character: ....

Behaviour: ....

....

b) In Chapter 23, the monster kills Frankenstein's new wife, Elizabeth.
Find an example of a character who behaves in a similar way in Chapter 20.

Character: ....

Behaviour: ....

....

Q2 Fill in the table below with examples from different parts of the novel that illustrate the key point about each character. You can either use quotes or just explain what happens, as long as it's a precise example.

Character	Key Point	Example One	Example Two
Frankenstein	Passionate and obsessive		
Elizabeth	Pure and virtuous		
The monster	An outsider		

Practice Questions

That's the end of the "Who's who", but you're not done yet. Here's a whole bunch of practice questions for you to get stuck into. If you really want to test yourself, pretend you're doing the exam for real. Remember to keep quotes concise and relevant — no one likes it when people drone on, and on, and on...

Q1 Using the passage below to help you, explain how Shelley presents the relationship between Victor Frankenstein and Clerval in the novel.

Taken from Chapter 19

But a blight had come over my existence, and I only visited these people for the sake of the information they might give me on the subject in which my interest was so terribly profound. Company was irksome to me; when alone, I could fill my mind with the sights of heaven and earth; the voice of Henry soothed me, and I could thus cheat myself into a transitory peace. But busy, uninteresting, joyous faces brought back despair to my heart. I saw an insurmountable barrier placed between me and my fellow men; this barrier was sealed with the blood of William and Justine, and to reflect on the events connected with those names filled my soul with anguish.

But in Clerval I saw the image of my former self; he was inquisitive and anxious to gain experience and instruction. The difference of manners which he observed was to him an inexhaustible source of instruction and amusement. He was also pursuing an object he had long had in view. His design was to visit India, in the belief that he had in his knowledge of its various languages, and in the views he had taken of its society, the means of materially assisting the progress of European colonization and trade. In Britain only could he further the execution of his plan. He was for ever busy, and the only check to his enjoyments was my sorrowful and dejected mind. I tried to conceal this as much as possible, that I might not debar him from the pleasures natural to one who was entering on a new scene of life, undisturbed by any care or bitter recollection. I often refused to accompany him, alleging another engagement, that I might remain alone. I now also began to collect the materials necessary for my new creation, and this was to me like the torture of single drops of water continually falling on the head. Every thought that was devoted to it was an extreme anguish, and every word that I spoke in allusion to it caused my lips to quiver, and my heart to palpitate.

Q2 Read Chapter 15 from "**As I read, however**" to "**imbued with different sensations**".

a) Explain how the monster is presented by Shelley in this extract.

b) In this extract, the monster discusses what he has learnt from books.
How is knowledge presented by Shelley in other parts of the novel?
You should write about:
  • why different characters seek knowledge
  • what effects knowledge has on characters.

Q3 Read Chapter 22 from "**You well know**" to "**no other happiness**". Explore the way Shelley presents Elizabeth's good qualities in this extract and in the novel as a whole.

Q4 Read Chapter 21 from "**My father was enraptured**" to "**my wasted frame**".
How far is Alphonse presented as a good father in *Frankenstein*?
You should write about:
  • how Alphonse is presented in this extract
  • how Alphonse is presented in the novel as a whole.

Section Three — Context and Themes

Influences and Literary Sources

Q1 Complete the passage below using words from the box. Each gap needs a different word.

Rousseau was an 18th-century philosopher. He believed that someone who grew up without

the company or guidance of others would be .... by society's prejudices.

This is reflected in Frankenstein — the monster is rejected first by .... and

then by the .... family. As a result, he becomes ....

and commits evil acts, including the .... of innocent people.

| Frankenstein scared compassionate torture cruel corrupted De Lacey Walton murder |

Q2 Decide whether each statement is **true** or **false**.

	True	False
Mary Shelley was influenced by the 'Romantic' movement.	☐	☐
The 'Romantics' believed that exposure to nature was damaging.	☐	☐
'Romantic' writing tends to be detached and unemotional.	☐	☐
The characters in *Frankenstein* are inspired and revived by the natural world.	☐	☐

Q3 Read Chapter 15 from "**But *Paradise Lost***" to "**envy rose within me**". The monster compares himself to Adam and Satan. Give one similarity between the monster and each of these figures.

The monster and Adam: ....

....

The monster and Satan: ....

....

Q4 *Frankenstein* is also known as *The Modern Prometheus*. In mythology, Prometheus created man from clay. He was also punished by the god Zeus for stealing fire to give to humans, as the gods didn't allow humans to have it. With reference to the myth, explain why this title is appropriate.

....

....

....

Knowledge and Ambition

Q1 How does Frankenstein's desire for knowledge drive the events of the novel?

....

....

....

Q2 Find a quote from Chapter 4 to back up each of these statements.

Statement	Quote that shows this
a) The pursuit of knowledge can be consuming.	
b) Acquiring knowledge can lead to unhappiness.	

Q3 Read Chapter 15, from "**Another circumstance strengthened**" to "**I am solitary and abhorred**". How does the monster feel about what he learns in Frankenstein's journal? Why does he feel this?

....

....

....

Q4 Walton's ambition is to find a route through the Arctic. Answer the questions below.

a) How does Walton's ambition relate to events happening in Britain when the novel was written?

....

....

b) Why is Walton reluctant to listen to Frankenstein's warning about the dangers of ambition?

....

....

My ambitions involve a cup of tea and a biscuit...

Walton and Frankenstein are like two peas in a hyper-ambitious, knowledge-seeking pod. Think about how Walton's quest to the Arctic is similar to Frankenstein's mission to make a giant, scary man-thing.

Section Three — Context and Themes

Science and Creation

Q1 Complete the passage below using the correct words from the box.

In Chapter 5, Shelley describes the "**spark of being**" that gives the ....

life. This links Frankenstein's work to 18th and 19th-century experiments into the

.... of life. A scientist called Galvani passed an ....

through a dead frog and noticed that its legs twitched. Another scientist, Aldini, found similar

results when he experimented on a dead ....

end	origins	X-ray	battery	electrical current	soul	monster	human being

Q2 Read Chapter 7 from "**My journey was very melancholy**" to "**more than all, thy lovely lake**".
What effect does nature have on Frankenstein in this passage? Explain your answer.

....

....

Q3 Creating the monster reduces Frankenstein's enjoyment of nature.
Briefly outline what message this puts across to the reader.

....

....

Q4 Read from the start of Chapter 5 to "**I had so miserably given life**". How does
Shelley present the creation of the monster as unnatural and wrong in this extract?

....

....

....

....

....

....

© Alastair Muir/REX/Shutterstock

It's alive! It's al- ahem... sorry, just a little side project...

By creating life, Frankenstein sets himself up as a God-like figure with power over life and death. Write
a paragraph explaining how the events of the novel show that experimenting with creation is dangerous.

Family

Q1 Summarise the relationship between Walton and his sister. Support your answer with a quote.

....

....

Q2 Find a quote from Chapter 1 to back up each of the statements below.

    a) Victor Frankenstein is proud of his father.

....

    b) Alphonse and Caroline Frankenstein are loving parents.

....

Q3 Give one way that the De Lacey family is presented as caring in the novel.

....

Q4 Why is it ironic that Frankenstein speaks in detail about his parents' **"deep consciousness of what they owed towards the being to which they had given life"**?

....

....

Q5 'Frankenstein wouldn't have attempted to create life if he hadn't moved away from his family.' Do you agree with this statement? Explain your answer with reference to his family relationships.

....

....

....

....

....

The De Lacey family get along like a house on fire...

The women in the novel all play a similar role — they're all caring, maternal types who look out for their families. Think about how Caroline, Elizabeth, Justine, Agatha and Safie behave in similar ways.

Society and Isolation

Q1 Give two examples from Chapter 6 of the novel which show that society can be a positive force. Your examples could be events or information about characters.

1) ....

2) ....

Q2 How do people's reactions to the monster show that society can be cruel? Use a quote from the novel to support your answer.

....

....

....

....

© Alastair Muir/REX/Shutterstock

Q3 Decide whether each statement is **true** or **false**, and give an example to back up your answer.

a) Society in the novel is unequal.　　　　　　　　　　　　　　　**True:** ☐　**False:** ☐

Example: ....

b) Social contact is necessary to Frankenstein's well-being.　　**True:** ☐　**False:** ☐

Example: ....

c) The events of the novel suggest that society's laws are always fair.　**True:** ☐　**False:** ☐

Example: ....

Q4 Identify who said each of these phrases, then explain how their isolation makes them unhappy.

a) "I bitterly feel the want of a friend"　　　　　Said by: ....

Explanation: ....

b) "I longed to join them, but dared not"　　　　Said by: ....

Explanation: ....

Join my new secret society — if you can find us...

Read Chapter 17 from "**How is this?**" to "**a female who will accompany you in your exile**".
Explore the way Shelley presents the dangers of isolation in this extract and in the novel as a whole.

Prejudice

Q1 Read the final paragraph of Chapter 15. How does
Felix's reaction to the monster reveal his prejudice?

....

....

Q2 Give two more examples from the novel of people being prejudiced against the monster.

1) ....

2) ....

Q3 Decide whether each statement is **true** or **false**.

	True	False
It is only the monster's appearance that prejudices others against him.	☐	☐
The monster is angry about being chased out of the village in Chapter 11.	☐	☐
De Lacey's reaction to the monster shows that other people's reactions are unfair.	☐	☐
Safie overlooks the monster's appearance.	☐	☐
The monster is enraged by the De Lacey family's reaction to him.	☐	☐

Q4 'The monster's prejudice against others is more damaging than their prejudice against him.'
Do you agree with this view? Explain your answer, using evidence from the novel.

....

....

....

....

Q5 What message do you think Shelley wanted to convey about prejudice?

....

....

Don't judge a book by its... er, yellow skin and black lips...
Prejudice causes lots of things to go wrong in the novel — make sure you've got a good grasp
of who's prejudiced against who and what effects it has. It just might come up in the exam...

Revenge

Q1 Give two different reasons for the monster taking revenge on Frankenstein.

1) ....

2) ....

Q2 Revenge becomes an obsession for Frankenstein and the monster.
Fill in the table with one quote for each character that shows this.

Character	Quote
Frankenstein	
The monster	

Q3 Why do you think the monster kills Elizabeth rather than Frankenstein?

....

....

....

....

© Alastair Muir/REX/Shutterstock

Q4 Do you think the monster's murder of William Frankenstein is justified?
Explain your answer using evidence from the novel.

....

....

Q5 Read 'Walton, in continuation' from "**I entered the cabin**" to "**such as you cannot even imagine**".
What does Shelley suggest about the nature of revenge in this passage? Explain your answer.

....

....

....

I'm too nice to take revenge — but accidents do happen...

PRACTICE TASK

Imagine that you're the monster after you've just killed William Frankenstein. Write a short paragraph
explaining some of the reasons behind your decision to murder Frankenstein's younger brother.

Writing about Context

SKILLS FOCUS

Including relevant information about the context of the novel will help you to get a high mark in the exam. *Frankenstein* was written in the 19th century, when life in Britain was changing rapidly. You should have an understanding of what life was like then and how ideas about society and human nature were changing. You should also know how scientific developments were influencing people. This page will help you to practise linking contextual information to themes and ideas in the book.

Q1 Read the sample answer extracts below and underline the contextual information.

> **a)** The monster struggles to understand his identity in the novel. He sees similarities between himself and the biblical figures of both Adam and the "arch-fiend" Satan, but his inability to fully relate to either man or devil ultimately leaves him feeling miserable, confused and alone. When the monster compares himself to Adam, the first man God created in the Biblical book of Genesis, it emphasises how lonely he is as the only member of his species. Linking Frankenstein's creation of the monster to God's creation of Adam in this way would have made Frankenstein seem blasphemous to many 19th-century readers, as likening the monster to Adam suggests Frankenstein has made himself into a God-like figure.

> **b)** Shelley's ideas in *Frankenstein* may have partly been inspired by the scientific debates about the origins of life that were taking place at the time she was writing. In Chapter 5, Frankenstein manages to "infuse a spark of being" into his creation, which implies that he is using electricity to animate the monster. This suggests Shelley's writing was influenced by the tests Luigi Galvani and Giovanni Aldini had done in 1780 and 1803 that used electricity to move the muscles of dead organisms. However, by never describing Frankenstein's methods in detail, Shelley makes sure that the science in her novel cannot be completely disproved. This helps to create the novel's unsettling mood, which is a common feature of Gothic novels such as *Frankenstein*.

Q2 Write down a piece of context that could be included in the sample answer below.

> Explain the importance of the natural world in *Frankenstein*.

> Shelley presents nature as a powerful, calming influence in the novel. When the tragic deaths of William and Justine overwhelm Frankenstein in Chapter 9, he leaves society to search for tranquillity in the beautiful "Alpine valleys". He finds a brief respite from his sorrows as he realises that his existence and suffering is temporary compared to the "eternity" of the "immense" mountain scenery around him.

....

....

....

....

Section Three — Context and Themes

Practice Questions

So, that's that — another section of 'Frankenstein' done and dusted. But before you head off to create your own giant scary friend, have a go at these practice questions. Be sure to reward yourself every time you work some relevant info about the novel's context into an answer — a biscuit (or two) should do the trick.

Q1 Read the extract below, then answer the following questions.

a) Explain how Walton's ambition is presented by Shelley in this extract.

Taken from Letter 1

These reflections have dispelled the agitation with which I began my letter, and I feel my heart glow with an enthusiasm which elevates me to heaven, for nothing contributes so much to tranquillise the mind as a steady purpose — a point on which the soul may fix its intellectual eye. This expedition has been the favourite dream of my early years. I have read with ardour the accounts of the various voyages which have been made in the prospect of arriving at the North Pacific Ocean through the seas which surround the pole. You may remember that a history of all the voyages made for purposes of discovery composed the whole of our good Uncle Thomas' library. My education was neglected, yet I was passionately fond of reading. These volumes were my study day and night, and my familiarity with them increased that regret which I had felt, as a child, on learning that my father's dying injunction had forbidden my uncle to allow me to embark in a seafaring life.

These visions faded when I perused, for the first time, those poets whose effusions entranced my soul and lifted it to heaven. I also became a poet and for one year lived in a paradise of my own creation; I imagined that I also might obtain a niche in the temple where the names of Homer and Shakespeare are consecrated. You are well acquainted with my failure and how heavily I bore the disappointment. But just at that time I inherited the fortune of my cousin, and my thoughts were turned into the channel of their earlier bent.

Six years have passed since I resolved on my present undertaking. I can, even now, remember the hour from which I dedicated myself to this great enterprise. I commenced by inuring my body to hardship. I accompanied the whale-fishers on several expeditions to the North Sea; I voluntarily endured cold, famine, thirst, and want of sleep; I often worked harder than the common sailors during the day and devoted my nights to the study of mathematics, the theory of medicine, and those branches of physical science from which a naval adventurer might derive the greatest practical advantage. Twice I actually hired myself as an under-mate in a Greenland whaler, and acquitted myself to admiration.

---

b) In this extract, Walton recalls how he was influenced by his Uncle Thomas. Explore the importance of family in shaping a person's character in other parts of the novel. You should write about:
- the effects loving families have on characters
- the effects a lack of family has on characters.

Q2 Read Chapter 19 from "**In this retreat**" to the end of the chapter. How does Shelley present Frankenstein's creation as unnatural in this extract and in the novel as a whole?

Q3 Read from the start of Chapter 4 to "**an incident happened that protracted my stay**". Explore the importance of science in this extract and in the novel as a whole.

Q4 Read Chapter 16 from "'**It is utterly useless**'" to "**forked and destroying tongues**". To what extent does Shelley present society as being responsible for the evil acts of the monster? Refer to this extract and to the novel as a whole.

Structure, Narrative and Form

Q1 Explain how having Frankenstein narrate in the first person helps to engage the reader's attention.

....

....

Q2 In Chapter 5, Frankenstein has a dream about Elizabeth. What event does this dream foreshadow? Explain the effect that this foreshadowing has on the reader.

Event: ....

Explanation: ....

....

Q3 Why does Walton's friendship with Frankenstein make his narration less trustworthy? Use a quote to support your answer.

....

....

Q4 Read Letter 4. Give an example of each feature of the epistolary novel form listed in the table below. Then explain the effect each feature has on the reader. One has been done for you.

An 'epistolary novel' is a novel made up of letters, in this case letters from Walton to his sister Margaret.

Epistolary feature	Example	Effect on reader
a) The narrator seems to address the reader directly.	*"Will you smile at the enthusiasm I express concerning this divine wanderer?"*	It makes the reader feel more involved in the story.
b) The narrator's knowledge of the story is limited.		
c) The narrator reveals their immediate reaction to events.		

Bang! Bang! He shot the monster — an e-pistol-ary tale...

Imagine that Walton saved the monster from the ice instead of Frankenstein. Make some notes on how the story might be different if it was told to Walton from the monster's point of view.

Symbolism, Imagery and Setting

Q1 Fire is a symbol of knowledge in the novel. How does Shelley use the fire in Chapter 11 to convey ideas about knowledge?

....

....

....

....

Q2 Read Chapter 2 from "**When I was about fifteen**" up to "**utterly destroyed**".
What do you think the blasted tree in this extract symbolises? Explain your answer.

....

....

....

Q3 Find a quote from Chapter 7 where imagery of light is used to describe:

a) youth

....

b) the power of nature

....

Q4 Darkness is linked to mystery in the novel. Explain how this is shown through:

a) Frankenstein's work

....

b) the monster's earliest memories

....

Q5 Which of the following statements are true? Tick all the statements that apply.

Shelley uses biblical imagery to describe characters. ☐

Frankenstein is linked with images of both good and evil. ☐

The monster always describes himself using imagery of Hell. ☐

Imagery of corruption is used to describe the women in Frankenstein's family. ☐

Section Four — The Writer's Techniques

Q6 Explain how Frankenstein's relationship with natural surroundings changes as the novel progresses. Use a quote to support your answer.

....

....

....

Q7 Find a quote from Chapter 9 that shows nature's ability to heal Frankenstein. Explain how the imagery shows this.

Quote: ....

....

Explanation: ....

....

Q8 Complete the passage below using the correct words from the box.

Shelley's decision to set .... exploration in the ....

is significant, as the harsh and unknown environment creates an underlying sense

of .... The bleak setting also emphasises ....

suffering and .... when he first appears in the novel. This shows how

settings can help to establish a mood and create .... for the reader.

| Frankenstein's danger tension Walton's joy loneliness harmony Arctic calm |

Q9 Read from the start of Chapter 10 to "**solitary grandeur of the scene**". Explain how the setting reflects Frankenstein's mood in this extract. Use a quote to support your answer.

....

....

....

....

Shelley could've been a drummer — all that cymbalism...

It won't be enough to just say that 'Shelley uses darkness as a symbol of mystery' when you're in the exam — you'll need to explain the effect each technique has on the reader and how it achieves this.

The Gothic Novel

Q1 *Frankenstein* contains many features of a Gothic novel. For each Gothic feature listed in the table below, give an example from the novel.

Gothic feature	Example in *Frankenstein*
a) Something unnatural happens.	
b) The story takes place somewhere wild and remote.	
c) Someone is an 'outsider'.	

Q2 Read from the start of Chapter 24 to "**the head of the mourner**". Explain how each of the following Gothic features creates a sinister atmosphere in the extract.

a) Madness

....

....

b) Extreme emotion

....

....

c) Disturbing setting

....

....

Q3 Frankenstein and the monster are often presented as doubles of each other in the novel. Explain the effect this has on the reader.

....

....

....

Double, double toil and — wait, wrong workbook, sorry...

The setting often links to the type of atmosphere that Shelley wants to create. For example, using Gothic settings can create a gloomy tone, emphasise characters' misery and even unsettle the reader.

Language

Q1 Find short quotes to back up the following statements about Frankenstein's language.

a) In Chapter 8, Frankenstein uses sorrowful language.

....

b) In Chapter 10, Frankenstein uses exclamations to show his fury.

....

Q2 Complete the passage below using the correct words from the box.

Shelley uses lots of descriptive language. For example, the monster uses all

five .... to create a vivid image of his earliest ....,

and Walton uses a .... when he describes the monster's quest

for .... as throwing "**a torch into a pile of buildings**". This

emphasises how destructive the monster's behaviour was and echoes his

.... of the De Laceys' cottage in Chapter 16.

burning
metaphor
safety
simile
senses
revenge
rhyme
memories
discovery

Q3 Explain how the tone of Walton's language at the start of the novel is different to the tone of his language at the end. Use a quote to support your answer.

....

....

....

Q4 Read 'Walton, in continuation', from "**'You, who call**" to "**my thoughts no more**". Explain some of the ways the monster uses persuasive language in this extract.

....

....

....

I metaphor-legged monster — Victor says he's 'armless...

Read Chapter 7 from "**Yet, as I drew nearer home**" to "**this thy dirge!**" **Explore the way Shelley presents Frankenstein's emotions.** You should write about:
- how Frankenstein's emotions are presented in this extract
- how Frankenstein's emotions are presented in the novel as a whole.

Working with Extracts

In the exam, you'll be given an extract from the book to analyse. The examiner is expecting you to write about the extract in detail, so it's important that you think about it carefully before you begin to write your answer. This page will help you to develop the main skills that you'll need. The extract here is shorter than the one you'll get in the exam, but it still provides useful practice. When you're writing in the exam, the P.E.E.D. method is your faithful friend — see p.15 for more.

Taken from Chapter 20

I trembled and my heart failed within me, when, on looking up, I saw by the light of the moon the dæmon at the casement. A ghastly grin wrinkled his lips as he gazed on me, where I sat fulfilling the task which he had allotted to me. Yes, he had followed me in my travels; he had loitered in forests, hid himself in caves, or taken refuge in wide and desert heaths; and he now came to mark my progress and claim the fulfilment of my promise.

As I looked on him, his countenance expressed the utmost extent of malice and treachery. I thought with a sensation of madness on my promise of creating another like to him, and trembling with passion, tore to pieces the thing on which I was engaged. The wretch saw me destroy the creature on whose future existence he depended for happiness, and with a howl of devilish despair and revenge, withdrew.

I left the room, and locking the door, made a solemn vow in my own heart never to resume my labours; and then, with trembling steps, I sought my own apartment. I was alone; none were near me to dissipate the gloom and relieve me from the sickening oppression of the most terrible reveries.

Q1 Read through the extract above and describe where in the novel it comes from. Think about what has just happened and what is about to happen.

....

....

....

Q2 In the extract, Frankenstein is described as "**trembling with passion**". Explain what this quote suggests about Victor's emotions.

....

....

Q3 Find an example of animalistic language in the extract and explain its effect.

....

....

Q4 In this extract, Frankenstein experiences feelings of isolation. Write down an example of another time in the novel when Frankenstein is isolated from other people.

....

Section Four — The Writer's Techniques

Practice Questions

Now that you've got yourself up to speed with the writer's techniques, it's time to have a go at these practice questions. Make sure you know what the question is asking you to do, and then set aside some time to do a rough plan before you start on your answer — otherwise you might end up in a bit of a pickle.

Q1 Using the passage below to help you, explain how Shelley presents revenge as a destructive force in *Frankenstein*.

> Taken from Chapter 16
>
> "Cursed, cursed creator! Why did I live? Why, in that instant, did I not extinguish the spark of existence which you had so wantonly bestowed? I know not; despair had not yet taken possession of me; my feelings were those of rage and revenge. I could with pleasure have destroyed the cottage and its inhabitants and have glutted myself with their shrieks and misery.
>
> "When night came I quitted my retreat and wandered in the wood; and now, no longer restrained by the fear of discovery, I gave vent to my anguish in fearful howlings. I was like a wild beast that had broken the toils, destroying the objects that obstructed me and ranging through the wood with a stag-like swiftness. Oh! What a miserable night I passed! The cold stars shone in mockery, and the bare trees waved their branches above me; now and then the sweet voice of a bird burst forth amidst the universal stillness. All, save I, were at rest or in enjoyment; I, like the arch-fiend, bore a hell within me, and finding myself unsympathised with, wished to tear up the trees, spread havoc and destruction around me, and then to have sat down and enjoyed the ruin.
>
> "But this was a luxury of sensation that could not endure; I became fatigued with excess of bodily exertion and sank on the damp grass in the sick impotence of despair. There was none among the myriads of men that existed who would pity or assist me; and should I feel kindness towards my enemies? No; from that moment I declared everlasting war against the species, and more than all, against him who had formed me and sent me forth to this insupportable misery.
>
> "The sun rose; I heard the voices of men and knew that it was impossible to return to my retreat during that day. Accordingly I hid myself in some thick underwood, determining to devote the ensuing hours to reflection on my situation."

Q2 Read Chapter 23 from "**The wind, which had fallen**" to "**rushed into the room**".
How does Shelley create tension in *Frankenstein*?
You should refer to this extract and to the novel as a whole in your answer.

Q3 Read Chapter 17 from "'**I intended to reason**" to "**I so ardently desire'**".
Explore the importance of companionship in *Frankenstein*.
You should write about:
- the importance of companionship in this extract
- how companionship is important to the novel.

Q4 Read Chapter 10 from "**Where had they fled**" to "**word may convey to us**".

a) Explain how the natural world is presented by Shelley in this extract.

b) In this extract, Frankenstein describes how his surroundings affect his mood.
How are settings used to influence characters' moods in other parts of the novel?
You should write about:
- how different settings have different effects
- how different characters react to their surroundings.

Understanding the Question

Underline key words in the question

Q1   Underline the key words in the following questions. The first one has been done for you.

a)   To what extent does Shelley present the monster as an evil character?

b)   Explain how the theme of revenge is presented in *Frankenstein*.

c)   Explain how Frankenstein changes throughout the novel.

d)   How is the theme of ambition presented in *Frankenstein*?

e)   Explore the importance of family in *Frankenstein*.

f)   Write about how Caroline's goodness is presented in *Frankenstein*.

g)   How does Shelley create an atmosphere of horror in the novel?

Make sure you understand exam language

Q2   Match each exam question to the correct explanation of what you would
need to do to answer it. You'll only need to use each white box once.

a) To what extent does Shelley present the monster as an evil character?	**1)** Analyse how Shelley writes about an aspect of a character in the novel.
b) How is the theme of ambition presented in *Frankenstein*?	**2)** Analyse the techniques Shelley uses to produce a certain effect.
c) Write about how Caroline's goodness is presented in *Frankenstein*.	**3)** Analyse how a theme contributes to the novel's plot and message.
d) Explore the importance of family in *Frankenstein*.	**4)** Analyse how far a description of a character in the novel is correct.
e) How does Shelley create an atmosphere of horror in *Frankenstein*?	**5)** Analyse the way Shelley writes about a theme in the novel.

Knowing what you need to do prevents confusion. Or does it?...

Understanding what the question is asking you to do is the first step towards writing a great answer. That's why
it's important to take your time in the exam, read the question carefully and make sure you're on the right track.

Making a Rough Plan

Jot down your main ideas

Q1 Look at the exam question below, then complete the spider diagram with at least three more main points for answering it.

Don't forget to underline the key words in the question before you start.

The monster uses eloquent language when he talks to Frankenstein.

> Read Chapter Seventeen from "**His words had a strange effect**" to "**'I shall appear'**". How is the monster presented as intelligent by Shelley in this extract and in the novel as a whole?

Put your main points and examples in a logical order

Q2 Choose your three main points from Q1 and fill in the plan below, adding evidence (a quote or an example from the text) for each point.

(Introduction)

Point One: ....

Evidence: ....

Point Two: ....

Evidence: ....

Point Three: ....

Evidence: ....

(Conclusion)

Make sure in a logical order you keep your points...

It's a good idea to spend five minutes or so on a rough plan before you start writing — keep referring back to it while you're writing your spectacularly brilliant essay so you don't lose your thread and go off on a tangent.

Making Links

Make links with other parts of the text

Q1   Look at the exam question and the table below. Complete the table with other relevant parts of the text which could be used to back up each point.

> Explore how ideas about human nature are presented in *Frankenstein*.

Point	Example 1	Example 2
People are shown to be prejudiced.	In Chapter 11, the villagers reject the monster because of his appearance.	
People can be selfless.	De Lacey's children sometimes go hungry so their father can eat.	
People need companionship and love.	The monster's solitude causes him pain.	

Extend your essay with other examples

You won't have time to do really detailed planning in the exam, so you should get into the habit of quickly thinking of links when you're doing practice questions.

Q2   Look back at the points you included in your plan in Q2 on p.43. For each point, write down another example from a different part of the text that you could include in your essay.

Example for Point One: ....

....

Example for Point Two: ....

....

Example for Point Three: ....

....

Learn examples in advance or your links will be off the cuff...

Making links helps you to compare and contrast how themes and characters are presented at different points in the novel. It also helps you to show the examiner that you know the book inside out and back to front.

Structuring Your Answer

P.E.E.D. stands for Point, Example, Explain, Develop

Q1 Read the following extract from an exam answer. Label each aspect of P.E.E.D.

Frankenstein is taken over by his desire to get revenge on the monster. This is shown when he tells Walton that his "vengeance" is "like a mighty tide". The word "mighty" shows that Frankenstein's desire for revenge is extremely strong. The way the simile compares it to a powerful natural occurrence also implies that it is unstoppable. By showing the extent of Frankenstein's fury, Shelley gives the reader a better understanding of why he pursues the monster so far for so long.

Embedding quotes is a great way to give evidence

Q2 Rewrite the following sentences so that a short part of the quote is embedded in each one.

a) The monster told himself he'd talk calmly with Frankenstein — "**I intended to reason**".

....

b) Frankenstein's spirits are low on his way home — "**My journey was very melancholy**".

....

Structure your answer using the P.E.E.D. method

Q3 Use the P.E.E.D. method to structure a paragraph on your first point from Q2 on p.43.

Point: ....

....

Example: ....

....

Explain: ....

....

Develop: ....

....

Wow your mates — tell them you P.E.E.D. all over the exam...

Using the P.E.E.D. method might take a little bit of getting used to, but it's definitely worth the effort. It'll help you to structure your paragraphs well and best of all, it'll encourage you to write well-developed answers.

Introductions and Conclusions

Give a clear answer to the question in your introduction

Q1 Read the introductions below, then decide which is better. Explain your choice.

> How is the monster presented by Shelley as deserving of sympathy in *Frankenstein*?

a)
> Shelley presents the monster sympathetically in the novel. For example, in Chapter Eleven he is described as a "poor, helpless, miserable wretch", encouraging the reader to feel sorry for him. At the end of the novel, despite him having killed several people, the reader still pities him. This shows that he is a complex character who challenges readers' expectations.

b)
> Shelley frequently encourages the reader to sympathise with the monster in *Frankenstein*. She makes him seem pitiable by presenting him as an innately good person who is driven to evil by repeated abuse. She also clearly links the monster's good nature to naivety and wonder, which emphasises his innocence to the reader.

Better Intro: .... Reason: ....

....

....

....

Don't write any new points in your conclusion

Q2 Read this conclusion to the exam question in Q1, then explain how it could be improved.

> To conclude, Shelley presents the monster as increasingly unlikeable as the novel progresses. However, in the final chapter, the monster says he "shall die" because Frankenstein has. This suicidal decision emphasises the monster's misery and the reader is ultimately left feeling sorry for him.

....

....

....

....

....

Hello there, I'm Frederick. Always start with an introduction...

Test your skills by writing an introduction and a conclusion for the exam question on p.43. Think about the good and bad examples on this page and use the points from your spider diagram to form your main ideas.

Writing about Context

Make sure you can link the novel to its context

Q1 Match each statement with the relevant contextual information.

> **a)** Frankenstein refers to life as "a spark of being".

> **b)** In the novel, the natural world is often described as beautiful and peaceful.

> **c)** The monster often compares himself to Satan and Adam.

> **1)** In the late 1700s and early 1800s, the 'Romantic' movement presented nature as a divine and majestic force.

> **2)** In the early 19th century, scientists were experimenting with using electricity to animate dead bodies.

> **3)** *Frankenstein* draws on John Milton's poem *Paradise Lost,* which is inspired by the Biblical book of Genesis.

Include context in your answer

Q2 Read the sample answer below, underlining the contextual information.

> Shelley uses Frankenstein's character to highlight that there are things humans shouldn't know. In Chapter Four, Frankenstein admits he "pursued nature to her hiding-places." This implies his experiments were unnatural by suggesting he has learnt things about nature which should have been kept secret. These ideas about hidden knowledge link to the novel's alternative title, 'The Modern Prometheus', which is inspired by Greek and Roman mythology. In the myth, Prometheus steals fire from the gods to give it to humans, despite the gods forbidding him to do so. By creating a parallel between Frankenstein and Prometheus, Shelley hints Frankenstein's experiments are unholy as well as unnatural.

Q3 Write a paragraph using your second point from p.43.
Include contextual information and use the P.E.E.D. method.

....

....

....

....

....

....

The monster's conned by texts — he thinks they're all factual...

Including some context will help you to get a good mark in your exam. Think about how life in the early 19th century might have shaped Shelley's ideas and how she conveys these ideas to the reader in *Frankenstein*.

Linking Ideas and Paragraphs

Link your ideas so your argument is easy to follow

Q1 Rewrite the sample answer below so that the ideas are clearly linked.

> Henry Clerval is presented in an idealised way to the reader. Henry Clerval is described as being "perfectly humane" and "full of kindness". Clerval contrasts with Frankenstein, who appears more and more selfish. This emphasises Clerval's goodness. Clerval's death is very shocking for the reader because he is shown to be so virtuous.

....

....

....

....

....

Q2 Write a paragraph using your third point from p.43. Make sure your ideas are properly linked.

....

....

....

....

....

Show how your paragraphs follow on from each other

Q3 Look at the three paragraphs you have written on pages 45, 47 and in Q2 on this page. Write down linking words or phrases you could use to link them together in your answer.

Paragraphs to link	Linking word or phrase
p.45 and p.47	
p.47 and p.48	

Linking phrases are like sat nav directions, only less annoying...

Linking phrases are great, but only if your ideas are in a logical order to begin with. That's why it's useful to make a plan — it doesn't have to be really detailed, but it's good to know where you're going before you start.

Marking Answer Extracts

Get familiar with the mark scheme

Grade band	An answer at this level...
8-9	• shows an insightful and critical personal response to the text • closely and perceptively analyses how the writer uses language, form and structure to create meaning and affect the reader, making use of highly relevant subject terminology • supports arguments with well-integrated, highly relevant and precise examples from the text • gives a detailed exploration of the relationship between the text and its context • uses highly varied vocabulary and sentence types, with mostly accurate spelling and punctuation
6-7	• shows a critical and observant personal response to the text • includes a thorough exploration of how the writer uses language, form and structure to create meaning and affect the reader, making use of appropriate subject terminology • supports arguments with integrated, well-chosen examples from the text • explores the relationship between the text and its context • uses a substantial range of vocabulary and sentence types, with generally accurate spelling and punctuation
4-5	• shows a thoughtful and clear personal response to the text • examines how the writer uses language, form and structure to create meaning and affect the reader, making some use of relevant subject terminology • integrates appropriate examples from the text • shows an understanding of contextual factors • uses a moderate range of vocabulary and sentence types, without spelling and punctuation errors which make the meaning unclear

Have a go at marking an answer extract

Q1 Using the mark scheme, put the sample answer extract below in a grade band and explain why.

> Explore how the relationship between Victor Frankenstein and Elizabeth is presented in *Frankenstein*.

> Shelley presents Frankenstein and Elizabeth's relationship as being very close. After Elizabeth is adopted, Frankenstein believes that, "till death", she will belong to him alone. This emphasises the intensity of his feelings and shows how closely linked their lives are. This also hints that their relationship may have a tragic end, which is confirmed later in the novel.

Grade Band: ....   Reason: ....

....

....

....

Marking Answer Extracts

Have a look at these extracts from answers to the question on p.49

Q1 For each extract, say what grade band you think it is in, then underline an example of where it meets each of the mark scheme criteria. Label each underlined point to show what it achieves.

---

a) Shelley uses the novel's epistolary form to show that Frankenstein and Elizabeth both love each other. Frankenstein's love for Elizabeth is made clear by Walton's letters, which relay Frankenstein's thoughts directly to the reader. Elizabeth's embedded letters in Chapter Six and Chapter Twenty-Two reveal her own point of view, for example, she calls Frankenstein "My dearest". These letters enable the reader to get a reliable indication of Elizabeth's affection as well as Frankenstein's. The epistolary form therefore allows Shelley to show their mutual love to the reader. Elizabeth's second letter to Frankenstein also reveals her willingness to defy their parents' wishes in order to ensure Frankenstein's happiness. Even though her parents have planned their union since their childhood, Elizabeth says she won't marry Frankenstein if it will make him unhappy. Challenging her parents in this way would probably have been seen as bold and daring behaviour for a woman at the time the novel is set. This shows the strength of Elizabeth's love for Frankenstein.

Shelley presents Elizabeth's love for Frankenstein as stronger than his love for her. In Chapter Three, Frankenstein describes Elizabeth's "entreaties" for him to "write often" and later, in Chapter Six, Elizabeth ends her letter with the command "I entreat you, write!" This near repetition shows how eager Elizabeth is to hear from Frankenstein, which emphasises how much she loves him. It also gives the reader the impression that Frankenstein has neglected Elizabeth, as she has to beg him to write to her. As a result, Shelley highlights the consistent nature of Elizabeth's love in contrast to Frankenstein's. The way her second request is more direct further reiterates the strength of her love for Frankenstein to the reader, as it gives her concern for him more urgency.

Grade Band: ....

---

b) Frankenstein and Elizabeth's relationship is presented as unsuitable. Elizabeth is described as being "heaven-sent", with hair of the "brightest living gold", a "saintly soul" and "celestial eyes". These adjectives associated with divinity present Elizabeth as angelic and, by describing several different parts of her as heavenly, Shelley suggests that Elizabeth is good through and through. This contrasts her with Frankenstein, who is engrossed "heart and soul" in his act of "filthy creation". The opposition between Frankenstein's corruption and Elizabeth's holiness emphasises what a poor match they are for each other. 19th-century readers may have felt this mismatch more keenly, as Frankenstein's creation of the monster challenges God's authority. This would have caused readers in the more devoutly Christian society of the time to believe Frankenstein was condemned to Hell. Shelley also uses Elizabeth's purity to hint that her relationship with Frankenstein will be short-lived. Emphasising Elizabeth's divine goodness suggests that she is too good for the corrupted world around her, which implies that she will struggle to survive in it for long.

The relationship between Frankenstein and Elizabeth is also presented as important to Frankenstein's well-being. In Chapter Two, Elizabeth is described as being able to "subdue" Frankenstein's violent temper, which suggests her presence has a calming effect on him. After her death in Chapter Twenty-Three, Frankenstein loses control over his rage and devotes himself to revenge. This turning point shows that without Elizabeth, Frankenstein's more intense passions overwhelm him and diminish his mental stability. His relationship with Elizabeth can therefore be said to represent his main link to goodness and self-control.

Grade Band: ....

Marking a Whole Answer

Q1 Read the sample answer below. On page 52, put it in a grade band and explain your decision.

> Read Chapter Three from "**'The ancient teachers'**" to "**I believed myself to possess a natural talent.**" How is Frankenstein presented as ambitious by Shelley in this extract and in the novel as a whole?

If it helps you, label examples of where the answer meets the mark scheme criteria.

In *Frankenstein*, Shelley presents Victor Frankenstein's ambition through imagery of power and Biblical references. By linking Frankenstein's ambition to power and religion, Shelley emphasises how strongly ambition motivates him. Frankenstein's ambition is also shown through comparisons with Robert Walton and the novel's epistolary form. By making Frankenstein's ambition such a fundamental part of the text, Shelley highlights the potential dangers of ambition to her readers, as she presents Frankenstein's excessive ambition as ultimately bringing the events of the novel to a tragic conclusion.

Shelley presents Frankenstein as determined to succeed in the extract. He says he will do "far more" than others and speaks in a purposeful and enthusiastic tone, stating he "will pioneer", "explore" and "unfold to the world" new knowledge. As "unfold" suggests something being opened, combining it with language of adventure like "pioneer" and "explore" implies that Frankenstein sees it as his quest to uncover ground-breaking secrets. The assertive "will", emphasises his ambition to the reader by highlighting his resolve to succeed even though his objective is unprecedented. This encourages the reader to admire Frankenstein's ambition at first, as his unwillingness to accept failure as an option helps him to achieve his goals. However, Shelley encourages the reader to reassess their values later in the novel when it's clear that Frankenstein's ambition to succeed at all costs causes the destruction of himself and everything he loves. This could imply Shelley only saw ambition as positive when it is kept in moderation.

In the extract, Frankenstein is taken over by his ambition. To illustrate this, Shelley describes Frankenstein as a musical instrument. The ambition inspired by the professor's words touches "various keys" and sounds "chord after chord" within him. This metaphor suggests that Frankenstein is a tool for his ambition to use, and that his ambition is strong enough to manipulate and control him. However, Shelley's presentation of Frankenstein merely needing to be "touched" by the professor's words also implies that his ambition is an inherent part of his character which just needed to be awoken. This complicates Frankenstein's presentation of himself as a victim by suggesting it is his own ambitious nature which destroys him, not "fate". As a result, the reader is prompted to consider how responsible he is for his own actions.

In the novel, Gothic doubles also contribute to the presentation of Frankenstein as ambitious. Frankenstein and Walton can be seen as Gothic doubles, which encourages the reader to compare their ambitious natures. Walton has an ambition to explore the Arctic, and he begins the novel with a "burning ardour" in his soul, which links to the "unremitting ardour" with which Frankenstein begins creating the monster in Chapter Four. By using the same word to describe the passion of both men, Shelley shows how they are each similarly driven by ambition. However, Walton is willing to abandon his ambitious aims, in contrast to Frankenstein who dies still wondering if "another may succeed" where he failed. This emphasises Frankenstein's ambition by showing that he can't control it, despite it causing him harm. Frankenstein's ambition is also emphasised by the character of Henry Clerval, who can also be seen as a Gothic double of Frankenstein. He is ambitious in a moderate and selfless way, which makes Shelley's presentation of Frankenstein's selfish ambition more apparent to the reader.

This answer continues on p.52. ➡

Marking a Whole Answer

Shelley also presents Frankenstein as ambitious by showing him trying to be like God. He refers to himself as the "father" and "creator" of a "new species", and the monster also refers to himself as Frankenstein's "Adam". These Biblical comparisons present the immense scale of Frankenstein's ambition to the reader, as he likens himself to God and aspires to emulate his ultimate power. The grand scope of Frankenstein's ambition may have been more evident to religious 19th-century readers, who probably would have found it blasphemous to see Frankenstein arrogantly assuming the role of God, especially given his many immoral deeds.

Shelley presents Frankenstein's ambition as the cause of his downfall. Throughout the novel, his aspirations cause him to suffer symptoms of illness. For example, he finds himself "oppressed by a slow fever" in Chapter Four, he falls down "in a fit" in Chapter Five, and he has an attack of "strong convulsions" in Chapter Twenty-One. This imagery of disease shows how Frankenstein's creation has disturbed his natural state, which hints that his aspirations exceed a human's usual limit. 19th-century 'Romantic' writers believed nature's beauty was restorative, which is reflected in the way Shelley presents nature as being able to soothe Frankenstein's anguish near the start of the novel. However, eventually nature fails to remedy the corrupting consequences of Frankenstein's ambition, which may suggest he has strayed too far from goodness to fully reverse the harm he has done to himself.

In addition, Shelley uses the novel's structure to highlight Frankenstein's ambitious nature. Shelley centres Frankenstein's ambition in the novel by embedding his tale inside Walton's letters, which allows Frankenstein to narrate in the first person. This emphasises Frankenstein's ambition as he takes over what ought to be Walton's narrative. As a result, the majority of "I" statements in the novel refer to Frankenstein, which reflects the way his ambition drives him to seek fame and glory. However, the monster's narrative is positioned as the literal 'heart' of the text, implying that the consequences of Frankenstein's ambition are more important than his ambition itself.

Overall, Shelley presents Frankenstein's ambition as an important feature of the text. It is presented through the novel's language, form and structure as well as in the tragic events that unfold in the plot. Though presented as a powerful form of motivation, causing Frankenstein to aspire to greatness, his ambition is also shown to be a harmful influence, making him very much a "cursed creator". This suggests that while ambition has its uses, if left unchecked it can overwhelm and corrupt a person's character completely, causing them to act against their faith, their society and ultimately, themselves.

Grade Band: .... Reasons: ....

....

....

....

....

....

....

Grade bands — when rock and indie just don't cut it...

It's no good ignoring mark schemes and grade bands — you should keep them in mind when you're writing your essays. That way, you'll get really familiar with what you need to do to get a good mark in the exam.

Writing Well

The examiners are ready and waiting to award you marks for writing well — so don't let the opportunity pass you by. Including a variety of vocabulary, relevant technical terms and different sentence structures will improve the quality of your writing. At the end of the exam, read through your work to check that you haven't made any spelling, punctuation and grammar (SPaG) mistakes. If you spot any, just cross them out and write your corrections neatly above. It's as simple as that.

Q1 Read the sample answer below. Underline the SPaG mistakes, then correct them. The first one has been done for you.

> Frankenstein's
> In the novel, <u>Frankensteins'</u> monster is described as being different too mankind.
>
> He says he can endure more extreme temperatures with "less injury' to himself,
>
> and that he can "subsist upon coarser diet" than humans can. Ultimately, these
>
> differences caused him disstress, as they make him feel "deformed" and alone,

Q2 Rewrite the following sentences, using appropriate language for the exam.

a) The monster doesn't want to be bad but people are horrible to him so he can't help it.

....

....

b) In the book, Frankenstein finds it hard to deal with a lot of the awful things that happen.

....

....

c) Justine's death shows how people can think bad things about others for no real reason.

....

....

d) Shelley refers to obsession a lot and Shelley shows how it can mess with people's lives.

....

....

Section Five — Exam Buster

Practice Questions

Here are some monstrous exam-style questions to sink your teeth into. Use the mark scheme on p.49 to help you write an answer or two — this should remind you of exactly what the examiners are looking for on the big day. Once you feel confident enough, have a go at the rest of the questions with no help at all.

Q1 Using the extract below to help you, explain how letters are important in *Frankenstein*.

> Taken from Chapter 6
>
> Clerval then put the following letter into my hands. It was from my own Elizabeth:
> "My dearest Cousin,
> "You have been ill, very ill, and even the constant letters of dear kind Henry are not sufficient to reassure me on your account. You are forbidden to write — to hold a pen; yet one word from you, dear Victor, is necessary to calm our apprehensions. For a long time I have thought that each post would bring this line, and my persuasions have restrained my uncle from undertaking a journey to Ingolstadt. I have prevented his encountering the inconveniences and perhaps dangers of so long a journey, yet how often have I regretted not being able to perform it myself! I figure to myself that the task of attending on your sickbed has devolved on some mercenary old nurse, who could never guess your wishes nor minister to them with the care and affection of your poor cousin. Yet that is over now: Clerval writes that indeed you are getting better. I eagerly hope that you will confirm this intelligence soon in your own handwriting.
> "Get well — and return to us. You will find a happy, cheerful home and friends who love you dearly. Your father's health is vigorous, and he asks but to see you, but to be assured that you are well; and not a care will ever cloud his benevolent countenance. How pleased you would be to remark the improvement of our Ernest! He is now sixteen and full of activity and spirit. He is desirous to be a true Swiss and to enter into foreign service, but we cannot part with him, at least until his elder brother returns to us. My uncle is not pleased with the idea of a military career in a distant country, but Ernest never had your powers of application."

Q2 Read Chapter 11 from "**'It was about seven**" to "**I had beheld in the village'**".

   a) Explain how society's reaction to the monster is presented by Shelley in this extract.

   b) In this extract, people's prejudice against the monster's appearance causes him to suffer. How is prejudice presented by Shelley in other parts of the novel?
   You should write about:
   • where prejudice occurs at different points in the novel
   • what effect prejudice has on characters in the novel.

Q3 Read Chapter 5 from "**Continuing thus**" to "**the land of knowledge**".
   Explore the way Shelley presents friendship in this extract and in the novel as a whole.

Q4 Read from the start of Chapter 9 to "**hide myself from his view**".
   'Shelley presents Frankenstein as a victim'. How far do you agree with this statement?
   Using this extract as a starting point, you should write about:
   • how Shelley presents Frankenstein's suffering in this extract
   • how Shelley presents Frankenstein in the novel as whole.

Section Five — Exam Buster

Answers

Section One — Analysis of Chapters

Page 2: Walton's Letters

1. He plans to sail across the Arctic Ocean.
2. a) True: e.g. "Heaven bless my beloved sister!" / "I love you very tenderly."
   b) False: e.g. "you have benevolently restored me to life"
3. E.g. Walton says they are "Shut in" by "ice" that stretches to the horizon. This suggests that their surroundings are oppressive and emphasises how remote the Arctic is.
4. The statements should be numbered 5, 2, 4, 1, 6, 3.

Page 3: Chapters 1 and 2

1. E.g. He admired her virtues and wanted to make up for her sorrows.
2. E.g. She longed for a daughter. / She knew she could give Elizabeth a better life.
3. a) E.g. She made him a kinder person: "she was there to subdue me to a semblance of her own gentleness."
   b) E.g. She encouraged him to be a good person: she "unfolded to him the real loveliness of beneficence".
4. E.g. He is attracted by its "real and practical" powers. He thinks it can help to satisfy the "fervent longing" he has to "penetrate the secrets of nature."
5. E.g. Shelley uses the metaphor of a "storm" that is "ready to envelop" Frankenstein to imply that something dreadful happened to him, without explaining what it is.

Task: Here are some points you may have included for the similarities between their youths:
   • Both were eager to learn from books.
   • Both had grand ambitions of achieving things that no-one had ever done before.
   • Both had loving families who took care of them.
   • Both are disappointed by their fathers' attitudes to their passions.
Here are some points you may have included for the differences between their youths:
   • Walton lost his father at a very young age, whereas Frankenstein grew up with his father present.
   • Walton was interested in exploration, whereas Frankenstein was interested in science.
   • Walton was interested in poetry at age 14, whereas Frankenstein was engrossed in science at that age.

Page 4: Chapters 3 to 5

1. The statements should be numbered 3, 1, 6, 4, 2, 5.
2. a) E.g. "the Angel of Destruction, which asserted omnipotent sway over me"
   b) E.g. "He heard with attention the little narration concerning my studies and smiled at the names"
3. E.g. He seems conflicted. Despite a growing sense of horror, he is still "urged on" by his desire to continue and succeed.
4. E.g. Once he brings the monster to life, he realises how monstrous he is and is terrified by what he has done. He is also upset that his dream has turned out to be ugly in reality.

Task: Here are some points you may have included:
   • Frankenstein finds a book about the works of Agrippa whilst on a trip. This sparks his interest in natural philosophy.
   • Professor Waldman's speech about natural philosophy fills Frankenstein with enthusiasm to uncover the "mysteries of creation."
   • At the end of his second year at university, Frankenstein discovers the secret to creating life.

Page 5: Chapters 6 to 8

1. a) E.g. "Excellent friend! how sincerely you did love me"
   b) E.g. "A serene sky and verdant fields filled me with ecstasy."
2. Frankenstein discovers that his brother has been murdered.
3. E.g. Describing the storm's "violence" and how lightning makes the lake look like a "sheet of fire" creates tension by making the landscape seem dangerous and threatening.
4. a) E.g. She wants to avoid going to Hell: "I confessed, that I might obtain absolution" / The priest bullies her into confessing: "He threatened excommunication and hell fire".
   b) E.g. His actions have indirectly caused William and Justine's deaths: they are his "first hapless victims".

Page 6: Chapters 9 and 10

1. E.g. It suggests that he feels too guilty to face other people, which implies that he feels ashamed of himself.
2. E.g. Frankenstein calls the valley "terrifically desolate", describing how the trees "lie broken", which makes the scenery seem empty and damaged.
3. a) False: e.g. "I trembled with rage and horror"
   b) False: e.g. "I expected this reception"
   c) True: e.g. "But I consented to listen"
4. E.g. The reader might see the monster as more human, as he is eloquent and reasonable. He offers to "be virtuous" if his wish is granted, which contrasts with his violent behaviour.

Task: Here are some points you may have included:
   • To create the impression that any joy Frankenstein might feel won't last for long.
   • To reflect Frankenstein's emotional turmoil at this point in the novel.
   • To keep the reader engaged, as it makes the narrative more varied and exciting.

Page 7: Chapters 11 and 12

1. E.g. To emphasise his natural innocence. It helps the reader to understand how much his character changes as a result of the hostility and rejection he experiences.
2. a) True: e.g. "A strange multiplicity of sensations seized me"
   b) False: e.g. "I examined the structure with great curiosity."
3. a) E.g. "I found, with pleasure, that the fire gave light as well as heat"
   b) E.g. "I discovered also another means through which I was enabled to assist their labours."
   c) E.g. "how was I terrified when I viewed myself in a transparent pool!"
4. E.g. He likes their "gentle manners" because he has only experienced cruel behaviour from humans before.

Page 8: Chapters 13 and 14

1. a) E.g. "I improved rapidly in the knowledge of language"
   b) E.g. "I heard details of vice and bloodshed, my wonder ceased and I turned away"
2. E.g. He recognises how different he is from the rest of society and begins to understand his status as an outsider. He understands this has made him miserable and wishes he could go back to being ignorant but happy.
3. E.g. Calling the De Laceys his "friends" and "protectors" in the hope that they might become those things.
4. kind, behaviour, selflessly, injustice, imprisoned, authorities, love

Task: Here are some points you may have included comparing Frankenstein's and the monster's relationships with knowledge:
   • Frankenstein has lots of possible subjects to study but focuses only on science, whereas the monster learns everything he can from a limited range of resources.

Answers

- Frankenstein wants to discover new knowledge, whereas the monster's knowledge comes from the books he finds and Safie's lessons that he eavesdrops on.
- Frankenstein views knowledge as a means of achieving great things, whereas the monster just wants to use it to understand his neighbours and communicate with them.

Here are some points you may have mentioned about knowledge being presented positively or negatively:
- Positively — Knowledge fascinates Frankenstein and prompts him to discover new things. / It allows the monster to understand society better and brings the monster pleasure.
- Negatively — Knowledge depresses the monster in Chapter 13, when he gains a new understanding of the world and his place in it. / It's dangerous, as Frankenstein's quest for knowledge leads him to irresponsibly create a life.

Page 9: Chapters 15 and 16

1. E.g. He is able to relate to its characters and compare himself to them.
2. E.g. Yes, because he seemed noble and forgiving before this, and accepted other outsiders such as Safie. **Or** e.g. No, because he is protective of his family and every human so far has reacted violently when they see the monster.
3. The statements should be numbered 4, 2, 3, 1, 5.
4. E.g. He likens himself to "a wild beast" that moves with "stag-like swiftness" and expresses anguish with "fearful howlings". This imagery makes the monster seem like an animal.
5. E.g. He thinks she will "curse" him on sight, as he assumes that Justine will be instantly prejudiced against him like William was. / He does it to get revenge on mankind, as he realises he is "for ever deprived" of their acceptance.

Page 10: Chapters 17 to 20

1. a) False: e.g. "I felt that there was some justice in his argument"
   b) True: e.g. "I took refuge in the most perfect solitude"
2. E.g. He dreads starting it, and once he finally begins, he has to force himself to continue despite his horror and disgust.
3. E.g. The monster has more power, as he commands Frankenstein to obey him. Frankenstein is now the one rebelling against his 'master' by refusing to obey his demands.
4. E.g. He threatens the monster then moves to attack him.
5. E.g. "You will know that soon enough". Any valid explanation, e.g. The townspeople's refusal to tell him anything feels hostile and threatening, which creates tension.

Page 11: Chapters 21 and 22

1. E.g. The boat Frankenstein arrives in is linked to the murder. / Frankenstein collapses at the sight of Clerval's body.
2. He thinks that the 'friend' is the monster.
3. E.g. His father's arrival calms him. It changes Frankenstein's feelings "from anguish to pleasure", and he starts to regain his health.
4. a) E.g. "Have you, then, some other attachment?"
   b) E.g. "but I will not listen to such a sinister voice"
5. E.g. Shelley hints at an approaching death without explicitly stating what will happen. She also uses the word "victim", which emphasises that someone is going to be hurt.

Page 12: Chapters 23 and 24

1. E.g. Shelley uses graphic imagery such as "distorted features" to create a vivid and shocking image of the damage done to Elizabeth's body.

2. E.g. He assumed that the monster would try to kill him rather than Elizabeth.
3. E.g. He dies of grief after hearing of Elizabeth's murder.
4. a) E.g. "a spirit of good followed and directed my steps"
   b) E.g. "you live, and my power is complete" / "a dead hare; eat and be refreshed"
5. E.g. To show the reader how the cycle of death and revenge has turned them both into 'monsters'. It also adds to the idea that their characters are Gothic doubles of each other.

Page 13: 'Walton, in continuation'

1. E.g. Frankenstein makes a speech to try to convince the sailors to carry on with Walton's voyage.
2. E.g. He suggests that he was influenced by "a high destiny", which implies that creating the monster was justified because he was being controlled by fate.
3. a) True: e.g. "Thus are my hopes blasted by cowardice and indecision"
   b) False: e.g. "your abhorrence cannot equal that with which I regard myself"
4. E.g. As Frankenstein is dying, he says he "did right in refusing" to finish the female monster, even though this led to Clerval's and Elizabeth's deaths. However, he is still determined to "destroy" the monster, which suggests he continues to feel guilt for creating him.

Task: You should have made a flowchart with arrows showing events that lead to Frankenstein's death. Here are some points you might have included:
- Frankenstein builds the monster out of dead body parts and brings it to life.
- He abandons the monster as soon as it wakes.
- To get revenge on Frankenstein, the monster murders Frankenstein's brother William and frames Justine Moritz, a family friend, resulting in her execution.
- Frankenstein begins to construct a female monster, but destroys it before it's complete.
- The monster kills Elizabeth on her and Frankenstein's wedding night in revenge.
- Frankenstein vows he will spend the rest of his life seeking revenge on the monster. He chases him to the Arctic, where he becomes stranded on ice and falls gravely ill.

Page 14: Skills Focus — Using Quotes

1. a - good, b - bad, c - good, d - bad, e - bad
2. Good quote usage: a), c) and e) [relevant and well embedded].
   Bad quote usage: b) [too long, not embedded] and d) [repeats point too closely].
3. You could have rewritten the examples as follows:
   b) The monster discovers that De Lacey came from "a good family in France" and that he was "respected".
   d) The monster calls Frankenstein his "cursed creator!" in an outburst of rage.

Page 15: Skills Focus — P.E.E.D.

1. a) The Develop stage is missing. E.g. This extreme comparison shows the extent of the monster's misery to the reader, as it makes his loneliness seem like torture.
   b) The Explain stage is missing. E.g. This shows how his mind starts losing its grip on reality because he isn't sure if his memories are real or imagined.
   c) The Example stage is missing. A specific example or quote should be added to back up the initial statement, for example: When Elizabeth falls seriously ill, Caroline nurses her back to health even though the disease is infectious.

Answers

Section Two — Characters

Page 16: Victor Frankenstein

1. true, true, false, false, false
2. E.g. "I never saw a man in so wretched a condition."
It shocks the reader and shows them how worn out he is.
3. E.g. He seems anguished and tortured by guilt. He uses emotional language and exaggeration which emphasises how deeply affected he is by Justine's murder trial.
4. Unforgivable — e.g. It's like he abandons his own child. It's his responsibility to take care of his creation.
Forgivable — e.g. He is horrified when faced with the reality of what he's done, so his reaction is understandable.
Task: Here are some points that you might have included:
   • In the extract, Frankenstein seems motivated by thoughts of his own success.
      - The word "success" is repeated throughout the passage.
      - Repetition illustrates self-absorption. Doesn't stop to consider if act of creation is morally right or wrong.
      - Symbolic of the novel as whole. Consistently puts his own needs first, fails to consider other points of view.
   • Victor is partly motivated by the thought of praise.
      - He says his creation would "bless" him.
      - Desire for gratitude shows he is acting selfishly.
      - Contrasts with God's loving motivation behind creating mankind.
   • Victor isn't completely selfish.
      - He "hesitated" and decides it's worth it to help "future" scientists learn from his experiment.
      - Shows that he doesn't just think about himself.
      - Links to end of novel when he dies hoping another will succeed where he failed.

Page 17: The Monster

1. a) E.g. This shows the reader that Victor thinks of the monster as more of a beast than a human.
   b) E.g. This suggests William sees the monster as frightening, hideous and dangerous.
   c) E.g. This implies that Walton thinks the monster is evil because "fiend" is another name for a devil.
2. E.g. The monster chooses to act selflessly. He goes hungry and stops stealing food when he realises it causes the De Laceys "pain". He also collects wood to help them.
3. a) E.g. "I now continually studied and exercised my mind"
   b) E.g. "my heart yearned to be known and loved"
4. E.g. The monster is angry with Frankenstein for neglecting him and driving him "from joy for no misdeed", but he still respects him, calling him "my natural lord and king".

Page 18: Robert Walton

1. a) E.g. "Inspirited by this wind of promise, my daydreams become more fervent" / "I feel my heart glow with an enthusiasm which elevates me to heaven"
   b) E.g. "do I not deserve to accomplish some great purpose?" / "I preferred glory"
   c) E.g. "I voluntarily endured cold, famine, thirst" / "I commenced by inuring my body to hardship."
2. E.g. Walton talks about his expedition using terms to do with adventure, such as "unexplored" and "dangerous mysteries", which conveys his excitement. He also uses the conditional tense in the final paragraph, which shows the reader he feels doubt and fear.
3. true, true, true, false
4. E.g. It shows that he can recognise the dangers of ambition. Even though he's "disappointed", he knows that pursuing his goal could hurt those around him, so he stops.

Page 19: Henry Clerval

1. E.g. This gives the reader the impression that he is courteous, kind and self-sacrificing, as the chivalric heroes in the books he reads often possess those qualities.
2. E.g. Clerval spends the evening with them all before Frankenstein goes to university. / At the end of Chapter 5, Clerval knows Frankenstein's family are worried about him.
3. b) E.g. He represents 'Romantic' ideas and takes great joy in nature.
   c) E.g. He is open-minded and eager to improve himself.
4. E.g. It might shock the reader because it seems unjust someone so good is killed. This could help the reader to empathise with Frankenstein's struggle to accept Clerval's death.
5. E.g. He is Frankenstein's foil. His "ardent affections" contrast with and emphasise Frankenstein's sorrow. His death also adds to Frankenstein's desire for revenge.
Task: Here are some points that you might have included:
   • In Chapter 5, Clerval looks after Frankenstein when he falls ill by being Frankenstein's "only nurse". This helps him to recover from his encounter with the monster.
   • In Chapter 18, the idea of Clerval accompanying Frankenstein abroad meant that he "rejoiced" despite his fear of the task ahead of him.
   • In Chapter 24, Frankenstein dreams of "Clerval enjoying health and youth", which gives him the strength to continue his journey north.

Page 20: Elizabeth Lavenza

1. E.g. She defends Justine during the trial in Chapter 8. / She puts Frankenstein's happiness before hers in Chapter 22.
2. b) E.g. The use of the religious terms "saintly" and "shrine-dedicated" imply that she is heavenly and pure.
   c) E.g. This suggests she is selfless. The word "veiled" implies she is hiding her suffering so she can help others.
3. E.g. To show the reader how much Frankenstein values her, as his thoughts dwell on her and return to her often. It also allows Shelley to emphasise Elizabeth's positive traits, which endears her more to the reader.
4. E.g. It suggests that she is treated like a possession by her family. It also hints at Elizabeth's passive role in the novel, as she has little ownership over what happens to her.

Page 21: Frankenstein's Parents

1. true, true, false, false
2. E.g. "His daughter attended him with the greatest tenderness"
The noun "tenderness" implies gentleness and the superlative "greatest" shows the depth of her kindness.
3. government, conflict, innocent, arrested, society
4. E.g. Yes, because they have "inexhaustible stores of affection" for Victor. Caroline also puts Elizabeth's needs ahead of her own and sacrifices her life to save her.
Or e.g. No, because they do not teach their son to take responsibility for his actions and Alphonse dismisses Victor's interests as "sad trash" instead of guiding them.
Exam Practice:
Your answer should have an introduction, several paragraphs developing different ideas and a conclusion. You may have covered some of the following points:
   • In this extract, Caroline is described as having a strong sense of responsibility towards society. Frankenstein maintains she considers it "more than a duty" to help the poor, describing it as a "passion". Linking her "passion" with a need to help others emphasises the strength

Answers

of her responsible attitude, and the way she sees her responsibility exceeding "duty" implies that her attitude is heartfelt. Making her attitude stand out to the reader early in the narrative helps Shelley establish the treatment of others in society as a central idea in the novel.

- Frankenstein takes no responsibility for the monster after creating him in Chapter Five. He "rushed out of the room" in "horror" as soon as the monster was animated, rejecting him because of how much the hideous reality differed to his own "beautiful" vision. Frankenstein's failure to accept the consequences of his experiment highlights his irresponsible attitude as a creator. This may reflect ideas about social responsibility at the time Shelley was writing, as people who were deemed different or 'socially unacceptable' were often refused support in society.

- Frankenstein feels responsible for protecting mankind from the monster. He ultimately refuses to make a female partner in case it leads to a whole "race of devils". Devils are traditionally associated with evil, so this metaphor suggests he is motivated by a desire to protect society from harm. However, it also highlights how inconsistent Frankenstein's attitude towards responsibility is, since he feels morally responsible towards society but not towards the monster.

Page 22: William and Justine

1. true, false, true, false
2. E.g. "I am resigned to the fate awaiting me."
   The word "resigned" implies that she accepts it's her destiny to die even though she is innocent, which shows great bravery.
3. a) E.g. Justine is one of the people who cared the most when William disappeared.
   b) E.g. She is forced into giving a false confession even though she is innocent.
4. E.g. Their deaths help to convince Frankenstein that the monster is evil. They increase his hatred of the monster, which continues the cycle of revenge and death between them.

Task: Here are some points that you might have included for William:
- As the reader knows very little about William, his goodness is the main thing that encourages the reader to feel sad when he dies.
- His goodness is used to show the reader the evil that the monster is capable of. William is described as a "sweet child" with angelic qualities. His innocence highlights the cruel and callous nature of his murder.

Here are some points that you might have included for Justine:
- Justine's goodness highlights Frankenstein's flaws to the reader. Her nursing of Caroline with "the greatest affection and care" contrasts with the lack of care Frankenstein shows towards the monster.
- Justine's goodness highlights the unfairness of society to the reader. Despite being "the most grateful little creature in the world", she is framed, blamed and killed for a crime she didn't commit. This encourages the reader to think critically about society and the legal system it uses.

Page 23: The De Laceys and Safie

1. b) E.g. He cares about his sister and tries to please her.
   c) E.g. She selflessly hides her troubles so her father thinks she is happy.
2. E.g. Although he is presented as kind and loving, he still has the same prejudices as everyone else the monster meets.

3. prejudice, religion, society, different, acceptance, rejection
4. E.g. De Lacey can't judge the monster on his appearance. He treats the monster fairly, proving that the monster could be accepted if people weren't prejudiced.

Page 24: Skills Focus — Making Links

1. a) Alphonse. E.g. He talks to Frankenstein about his home in Geneva and his family to try and make him feel better.
   b) Frankenstein. E.g. He destroys the female partner he was creating for the monster.
2. You could have used the following examples:
   Frankenstein — In Chapter 4 he recalls how he worked with "unremitting ardour." / He chases the monster to the North Pole to seek revenge.
   Elizabeth — She is described as "heaven-sent" in Chapter 1. / She implies Victor's happiness is more important than her own when talking about marriage in Chapter 22.
   The monster — In Chapter 10 he says he "alone" is "irrevocably excluded" from the happiness others feel. / He says he is "shunned and hated by all mankind" in Chapter 17.

Page 25: Practice Questions

Your answers should have an introduction, several paragraphs developing different ideas and a conclusion. You might have covered some of the following points:

1. • In the extract, Frankenstein is protective of Clerval. He tries to hide his suffering so that he doesn't diminish the "enjoyments" and "pleasures" Clerval experiences in Britain. This emphasises how much Frankenstein cares about Clerval because he chooses to suffer alone instead of introducing his misery to his friend's life. This protectiveness makes Frankenstein seem parental toward Clerval, which is an idea reinforced in the extract by the way he sees him as an "image" of his "former self".
   • In the novel, Clerval is presented as Frankenstein's foil. Clerval is described as having a "noble spirit" in contrast to Frankenstein who loses "all soul" except for the ambition which drives him to create the monster. This contrast between Clerval's virtuous spirit and Frankenstein's loss of spirit emphasises both the goodness of Clerval and Frankenstein's transgression. Society in 19th-century Britain was more religious than modern Britain and so may have considered moral goodness more important. Shelley's original readers may therefore have valued Clerval's virtue and condemned Frankenstein's corruption more strongly than readers today.
   • Clerval's relationship with Frankenstein is important to Frankenstein's well-being. When Clerval arrives in Ingolstadt in Chapter Five, Frankenstein feels a "calm and serene joy" for the first time in "many months". The use of two adjectives meaning 'peaceful' emphasises how soothing Frankenstein finds Clerval's presence, and linking the sense of peace to "joy" highlights how content Clerval makes him feel. After Clerval's death, Frankenstein says Clerval's spirit "consoles" him. This shows how Frankenstein still relies on Clerval to soothe his troubled state of mind, even after Clerval's death.

2. a) • In the extract, Shelley shows that the monster is confused about his identity. He asks himself a series of questions in quick succession, such as "Who was I? What was I?", but lacks the answers. This emphasises his uncertainty and shows his struggle to find his place in the world, as he is unable to relate to the people around him. The monster's lack of clear identity here allows Shelley to explore the impact society has on forming his identity later in the

novel. This also suggests that Shelley was influenced by the 19th-century philosophers like Rousseau, who questioned how society could affect someone's identity.

- In the extract, the monster is presented as impressionable. The ideas from his books take a "firm hold" on his mind and are responsible for his initial beliefs about right and wrong. The powerful impact the books have on him highlights his naivety because he lacks the knowledge or experience to question what he reads. The monster's impressionable nature also emphasises the similarity between him and his creator, as Frankenstein is shown to be impressionable in Chapter Two when he takes outdated philosophical ideas seriously.

- In the extract, the monster is presented as good-natured. From his reading, he develops "the greatest ardour for virtue" and an "abhorrence for vice". The contrast between the words "ardour" and "abhorrence" shows how principled he is, as he presents right and wrong as opposites. This makes it more poignant for the reader when the monster is later driven to perform evil acts by the abuse and misery he experiences.

b) • Shelley presents knowledge as desirable. In his letters, Walton says he hopes to discover a passage across the treacherous ice of the North Pole to achieve "glory". The fact that it would bring Walton "glory" and his subsequent willingness to put himself in danger emphasises how desirable the knowledge he seeks is. A 19th-century reader may have related to Walton's quest more easily than a modern reader, as many 19th-century British explorers sought fame and fortune in their attempts to find a route through the Arctic.

- Shelley suggests knowledge can be harmful. When the monster discovers his "accursed origin" in Chapter Fifteen he becomes "sickened". The imagery of illness suggests that learning the truth about his creation fills the monster with strong feelings of self-disgust. This reminds the reader of the "disgust" that fills Frankenstein's "heart" at the start of Chapter Five when he recognises the truth about the being he has created, highlighting the similarities between their characters to the reader.

- Shelley presents knowledge as bad when it's pursued selfishly. Walton begins the novel willing to "sacrifice" everything for the glory of discovering a new route through the Arctic. However, when he says this, a "dark gloom" passes over Frankenstein's face. This reaction makes Walton's desire to chase knowledge at any cost seem ominous. By the end of the novel, Walton refuses to lead his crew "unwillingly to danger". This shift in attitude suggests Walton develops a healthier balance between his pursuit for knowledge and his need for glory.

3. • The extract shows Elizabeth's good nature through her willingness to put Frankenstein's happiness before her own. She wants to marry Frankenstein but tells him their marriage is his "own free choice". All three of these words promote Victor's independence, emphasising how Elizabeth selflessly tries to have as little influence as possible in his decision. Elizabeth's goodness is further reinforced when she is contrasted with Frankenstein, who selfishly marries her despite knowing that it will summon the monster on their "wedding-night".

- Elizabeth's goodness is shown when she encourages Frankenstein and Clerval to be virtuous. In Chapter Two, she brings Frankenstein closer to "gentleness" and teaches Clerval "the real loveliness of beneficence". The loving language, shown in the nouns "gentleness", "loveliness" and "beneficence", gives Elizabeth an angelic quality which emphasises her virtue to the

reader. This presentation of Elizabeth as virtuous reflects 19th-century attitudes, as women were expected to be pure-hearted and chaste.

- Elizabeth is presented as loyal in Chapter Eight. She is the only person with enough faith in Justine's innocence to "come forward" to defend her reputation in court. Here, Elizabeth does what she believes is right even though it could damage her reputation, which emphasises how devoted she is to her friends. Reputation would be important to Elizabeth, as her adoptive father was a known public figure in Geneva. This reinforces the strength of her loyalty to the reader.

4. • In the extract, Alphonse is presented as a good father through his focus on his son's well-being. Alphonse tries to awaken "feelings of affection" in Frankenstein and wants "to delay" their departure from Ireland because he fears Frankenstein is too weak to travel. This highlights how Alphonse looks after both Frankenstein's mental and physical health. It also echoes the caring attitude he shows towards Frankenstein near the start of the novel, which presents his caring nature as consistent. This gives the impression Alphonse is a dependable father.

- Alphonse is presented as a loving father after William's death in Chapter Seven. When Frankenstein sees him, he describes the "unhappiness deeply impressed" on Alphonse's face. The word "impressed" emphasises Alphonse's love for William by suggesting his grief is etched on his face. The fact that it runs 'deep' also suggests that his grief is both genuine and profound. This also makes the way he represses his sorrow to greet Frankenstein "cheerfully" seem very selfless and brave, which underlines his fatherly nature to the reader.

- Shelley also presents Alphonse as a poor father at times. In Chapter Two, he "carelessly" dismisses Frankenstein's natural philosophy book as "sad trash". He doesn't take the time to explain the reasoning behind his criticism, which makes it seem like he doesn't care about guiding his son's learning. Shelley may have been trying to use this incident to warn readers about the dangers of unsupervised experimentation, as Frankenstein goes on to do most of his work alone without anyone to reign in his ambition. As science was beginning to play a bigger role in British society when Shelley wrote the novel, she may have been suggesting it should be carefully monitored.

Section Three — Context and Themes

Page 26: Influences and Literary Sources

1. corrupted, Frankenstein, De Lacey, cruel, murder
2. true, false, false, true
3. The monster and Adam: e.g. They are the only beings of their kind.
   The monster and Satan: e.g. They are both jealous of people who seem happier than them.
4. E.g. Both Frankenstein and Prometheus create life. Frankenstein wants this knowledge to benefit mankind, like Prometheus's gift of fire, and they are both punished for their actions.

Page 27: Knowledge and Ambition

1. Frankenstein wants to discover the secret to creating life, which leads him to create the monster. This action then influences all of the main events later in the novel.
2. a) E.g. "The summer months passed while I was thus engaged, heart and soul, in one pursuit."

Answers

b) E.g. "how much happier that man is who believes his native town to be the world"

3. E.g. The monster is "sickened" by what he learns from the journal. He regrets that he was ever created because he believes he is "so hideous" that he will always be alone.

4. a) E.g. In the early 1800s, there were several attempts to find a passage through the Arctic.

   b) E.g. Walton is obsessed with his quest, so he is determined to complete his voyage despite the dangers he's warned of.

Page 28: Science and Creation

1. monster, origins, electrical current, human being

2. E.g. The nature around him restores his peace of mind, as he goes from a state of "Fear" to one of "comparative happiness".

3. E.g. It suggests that humans should not 'play God' because it prevents them from engaging fully with natural creation.

4. E.g. Shelley describes the monster's "dull yellow eye" and "black lips", which emphasises his unnatural appearance. Frankenstein runs from his creation, and later dreams of death, which hints that he was wrong to create the monster.

Task: Here are some points you might have included:
   • Frankenstein has no control over his creation. After he gives it life, it develops its own thoughts and ideas. This shows that creation can have unforeseen consequences.
   • The monster that Frankenstein creates comes to hate him and murders his family and friends. This suggests that a being can turn on its creator.
   • Frankenstein is bound to the monster because he created it. This leads to his isolation, misery and eventual death.

Page 29: Family

1. E.g. They seem to be close, as he writes to her fondly. For example, he thanks her for all of her "love and kindness".

2. a) E.g. "my father had filled several public situations with honour"
   b) E.g. "I was their plaything and their idol"

3. E.g. Felix and Agatha go hungry so that their father can eat.

4. E.g. Frankenstein fails to do this himself. He doesn't acknowledge the responsibility he owes to the monster.

5. E.g. Yes, because Frankenstein's parents teach him "self-control", so if Alphonse had been there to reinforce this he would not have become obsessed with creating life. His family are also concerned about his well-being, so they would not have let him shut himself away for so long to complete his experiments. **Or** e.g. No, because his family make little attempt to understand his interests or rein in his passions, for example his father does not explain Agrippa's shortcomings but dismisses the work as "sad trash". This suggests that even if Frankenstein had remained at home, his family still wouldn't have intervened in his work.

Page 30: Society and Isolation

1. E.g. The Frankensteins take Justine in because her mother treated her badly. / Frankenstein helps Clerval to settle in Ingolstadt.

2. E.g. In the village, the residents "attacked" the monster without provocation. This shows that people's instinct is to hurt and drive out anyone who is different.

3. a) True: e.g. The De Laceys are poorer than the Frankensteins.
   b) True: e.g. He becomes unhappy and obsessive when alone.
   c) False: e.g. Justine is wrongly executed for murder.

4. a) Walton, e.g. He has nobody to discuss his plans with, or to share his joy.
   b) The monster, e.g. He longs for companionship but can't find anyone who will accept him.

Exam Practice:
Your answer should have an introduction, several paragraphs developing different ideas and a conclusion. You may have covered some of the following points:
   • In this extract, Shelley uses the monster to show that isolation can make people cruel. The monster states that his "vices are the children of a forced solitude", suggesting that if he had had a companion he would not have committed terrible crimes, such as William's murder. Shelley's negative presentation of isolation was probably influenced by the work of the 19th-century philosopher Rousseau. Rousseau believed that humans raised without positive social contact would be 'disfigured' by society's prejudices, and this belief supports the monster's view that his malice is a result of his isolation.
   • Through the character of Frankenstein, Shelley shows that isolation can cut people off from society's moral values. Frankenstein isolates himself from his friends and family to pursue his ambition. The resulting lack of moral guidance means that he doesn't question the dangers or ethics of creating a monster. The monster similarly claims that a companion will cause him to "become linked to the chain" of human feeling and therefore morality. The word "chain" reinforces the sense that humans are interconnected and cannot live virtuous lives in isolation.
   • Shelley structures the novel to reinforce the dangers of isolation. By using a frame narrative, she shows Walton, Frankenstein and the monster are increasingly affected by their isolation. While Walton's isolation makes him unhappy, Frankenstein's drives him towards "madness", and the monster's compels him to commit evil acts. This prompts the reader to compare the three characters and conclude that the greater the intensity of the isolation experienced, the greater the danger to the individual and society.

Page 31: Prejudice

1. E.g. Felix immediately attacks the monster rather than seeing if he's a danger, which shows that he is prejudiced against the monster because of the monster's appearance.

2. E.g. Frankenstein immediately abandons the monster. / William screams when he sees him and won't listen.

3. true, false, true, false, true

4. E.g. Yes, because the monster's prejudiced belief that "All men hate" him leads him to commit evil acts. For example, he plants the locket on Justine on the assumption that she will "curse" him, which leads to her death. **Or** e.g. No, because the monster is originally "susceptible of love and sympathy", and it is only through the prejudice of others that he becomes cruel. Therefore, other people's prejudice is the main cause of the damage the monster does.

5. E.g. It is wrong to be prejudiced against people on the basis of their appearance, and it can be very harmful.

Page 32: Revenge

1. E.g. To punish Frankenstein for abandoning him. / To make Frankenstein regret breaking his promise to help him.

2. Frankenstein: e.g. "I confess that it is the devouring and only passion of my soul."
   The monster: e.g. "revenge, henceforth dearer than light or food!"

3. E.g. Because he knows it will cause Frankenstein worse suffering. He also wants Frankenstein to feel the pain that he felt when Frankenstein destroyed the second creature.

Answers

4. E.g. Yes. Frankenstein deserves to feel pain like the monster did after Frankenstein "abandoned" him. **Or** e.g. No, because really he's angry at society and the De Laceys for rejecting him, and killing an innocent child is wrong.

5. E.g. Shelley shows that revenge is harmful to the person seeking it as well as the person they want revenge on. The monster has "destroyed" Frankenstein, but it has brought him "torture". / Shelley shows how powerful revenge can be. The monster feels "anguish" as he seeks revenge on Frankenstein, but he is unable to stop.

Task: You should have written your paragraph from the monster's point of view. Here are some points that you might have included:

- The monster learns that William 'belongs' to his "enemy", then declares that William will be his "victim". This suggests that the monster killed William to get revenge on Frankenstein.
- He knew that killing William would be an effective way to cause Frankenstein "despair" and "torment".
- He says he silenced William because the boy "loaded" him with "epithets" (terms of abuse). This suggests that the monster murdered William for being cruel towards him.

Page 33: Skills Focus — Writing about Context

1. a) You should have underlined: the first man God created in the Biblical book of Genesis / Linking Frankenstein's creation of the monster to God's creation of Adam in this way would have made Frankenstein seem blasphemous to many 19th-century readers.

   b) You should have underlined: the scientific debates about the origins of life that were taking place at the time she was writing / the tests Luigi Galvani and Giovanni Aldini had done in 1780 and 1803 that used electricity to move the muscles of dead organisms / which is a common feature of Gothic novels such as Frankenstein.

2. E.g. This presentation of nature's long-lasting magnificence shows how Shelley was influenced by the ideas of the 'Romantic' movement, which saw nature as a powerful, inspiring and restorative force.

Page 34: Practice Questions

Your answers should have an introduction, several paragraphs developing different ideas and a conclusion. You may have covered some of the following points:

1. a) • Shelley shows the reader that Walton's ambition is an important part of his character. He describes his voyage as "the favourite dream of my early years", which suggests that he had many ambitions to choose from. The reference to his "early years" also shows that Walton has been ambitious since he was a child, implying that ambition has always been a central aspect of his character. Highlighting the strength of Walton's ambition so early on in the novel helps Shelley to establish ambition as a key theme.

   • In this extract, Shelley presents Walton's ambition as persistent. He "voluntarily endured cold, famine, thirst, and want of sleep" whilst preparing for the voyage. Presenting these hardships as a list shows how many obstacles he has faced in the pursuit of his ambition, which increases the reader's sense of his persistence and determination. Walton's persistence at the start of the novel contrasts with his decision to turn back at the end, which demonstrates how his ambition has perhaps been restrained by Frankenstein's warning.

   • Shelley also presents Walton's ambition as unrealistic in this extract. He says that when he was a poet, he hoped

to be compared to the likes of "Homer and Shakespeare". Linking himself to such famous poets suggests he has an exaggerated idea of his own ability to succeed. This idea of Walton being overly ambitious may have been more evident to a 19th-century reader, as his attempt to trace a passage from Britain through the Arctic was something that nobody had successfully achieved at that time.

   b) • Shelley uses the monster's narrative to show how a loving family can shape how someone behaves towards others. After observing the De Laceys, the monster decides to "assist their labours" by fetching firewood. This shows how observing the De Laceys has taught the monster the value of being kind and respectful to others. However, the De Laceys also make the monster bitter. A key idea in the text is Rousseau's theory that society can corrupt an individual, which Shelley demonstrates through the De Laceys. Their unwillingness to extend kindness to the monster causes him to lose faith in humanity and become corrupted by jealousy and revenge.

   • Shelley suggests that being in close contact with a loving family helps to keep characters level-headed. Frankenstein's narration begins with two chapters that mention how his family taught him "patience" and "self-control" during his childhood. Frankenstein later becomes ill and obsessive once he is separated from his family. Structuring the novel in this way shows how important Frankenstein's family are in keeping him grounded, because as soon as they are apart his life descends into chaos. This idea emphasises the cruelty of Frankenstein's abandonment of the monster to the reader, as he is the only 'family' the monster has.

   • Shelley uses *Paradise Lost* to emphasise the negative effects of growing up without a family. In Chapter Fifteen the monster compares himself to Adam, stating that because Adam was looked after by his creator, he was "happy and prosperous" whereas the monster is "wretched, helpless, and alone". Using the adjectives "wretched", "helpless" and "alone" in quick succession emphasises how isolated the monster feels without Frankenstein's guidance. The contrast between the monster's loneliness and Adam's happiness highlights Frankenstein's irresponsibility as a creator, as it suggests his neglect is a main cause of the monster's misery.

2. • In this extract, Shelley suggests that Frankenstein's act of creation is wrong. He approaches his work "in cold blood" which suggests he has to shut off his emotions to continue making the female monster. The fact that he has to fight against his natural instincts implies that what he is doing goes against the laws of nature. In 19th-century Britain, creation was typically viewed as an act of God, so many 19th-century readers would have seen Victor's unnatural methods of creation as blasphemous. As Frankenstein's creation causes him to suffer, this highlights the role of *Frankenstein* as a cautionary tale warning readers about the dangers of challenging God's authority.

   • Shelley uses the setting in this extract to present Frankenstein's act of creation as artificial. Frankenstein goes to the Orkneys' "desolate and appalling landscape" to create the female monster away from prying eyes. The word "desolate" suggests that the scene is lifeless, which associates the landscape with a lack of fertility. This encourages the reader to consider Frankenstein's creation of the female monster there as unnatural. Later on in Chapter Twenty, Frankenstein supports this idea by referring to the female monster as "the thing" when he destroys it. His wording implies he sees her as a man-made object rather than a human.

Answers

- Throughout *Frankenstein*, Shelley associates creation with death. Frankenstein's materials come from the "damps of the grave" and the monster brings death to Frankenstein's friends and family. This suggests that Frankenstein's creation has upset the normal cycle of life by involving death in a process that should be about birth. This association with death makes the creation of the monster seem supernatural and disturbing, a concept which is a common feature of the Gothic genre Shelley adopts.

3.
- In this extract, Shelley shows the power that science has over Frankenstein. At university, Frankenstein becomes "engaged, heart and soul" in his scientific studies and does not return home for two years. His sudden neglect of his family contrasts with his previous closeness to them, which demonstrates the strong influence science has on his actions. The power that science has over Frankenstein is further emphasised by the way it blinds him to the reality of what he is doing until he succeeds in bringing the monster to life.
- Science is used to demonstrate that pursuing forbidden knowledge is dangerous. In the novel, Frankenstein's pursuit of "the principle of life" brings about his downfall because the monster causes the deaths of his best friend and most of Frankenstein's family. As a result, *Frankenstein* can be read as a warning to 19th-century scientists conducting experiments into life and death like those of Galvani and Aldini. By suggesting that such work strays into areas of 'forbidden' knowledge, Shelley may be implying that there will be severe consequences.
- In the novel, Shelley suggests that science threatens moral order. For example, Frankenstein takes dead bodies from their resting places, viewing a churchyard as "merely the receptacle of bodies deprived of life". The use of a clinical word like "receptacle" gives his comment a detached tone, which suggests his scientific approach involves no remorse for disturbing the dead. This immoral attitude would be shocking to any reader, but might have been more shocking to a 19th-century reader, as then such practices would have been considered widely as blasphemous.

4.
- Shelley uses the structure of *Frankenstein* to show that the monster's evil acts are partly a result of his poor treatment by society. By this point in the novel, the reader already knows about his evil deeds, but in this extract Shelley reveals that he only turned his "mind towards injury and death" after the De Laceys attacked him. Withholding information about society's role in the monster's downfall until this point increases its impact on the reader. This might encourage the reader to sympathise with the monster because it implies that he is not completely to blame for the evil acts that he commits.
- Shelley suggests that the prejudice that society has towards the monster is one of the main causes of his wrongdoing. Once the De Laceys reject him he immediately declares "everlasting war against the species", assuming that all humans are the same and will treat him cruelly. This shows that society's prejudice has taught him to respond with prejudice of his own. Shelley was influenced by the philosopher Rousseau's argument that people who are abandoned at birth, without guidance or instruction, would become prejudiced against society. This is precisely what happens to the monster in *Frankenstein*.
- Shelley also presents the monster as partly responsible for his evil actions. In this extract, the monster allows himself to "be borne away by the stream" of "revenge and hatred" that he feels after the De Laceys reject him.

The phrase "allowing myself" suggests to the reader that the monster has the ability to control his emotional response, but he chooses to give in to the anger which leads to him burning the De Laceys' cottage. Shelley also presents the monster as responsible for his evil choices in Chapter Seventeen when he declares, "if I cannot inspire love, I will cause fear", as this implies his later evil acts were premeditated.

Section Four — The Writer's Techniques

Page 35: Structure, Narrative and Form
1. E.g. Using the first person gives Frankenstein's narration immediacy and lets the reader see his thoughts.
2. Elizabeth's death in Chapter 23.
E.g. It builds the reader's anticipation because they think she's going to die but don't know when or how.
3. E.g. Because Walton's "affection" for Frankenstein could make him unwilling to present his friend in a negative way.
4. b) E.g. Walton is confused when Frankenstein wants to journey further into the Arctic. / It makes the reader want to find out more.
   c) E.g. "So strange an accident has happened to us that I cannot forbear recording it". / It makes the narrative more exciting for the reader.
Task: Here are some points you may have included:
- Frankenstein might be presented less sympathetically. He could be described respectfully for creating the monster, but criticised for not making a female as well.
- The destruction of the female monster might be made to seem cruel and treacherous instead of necessary.
- It might be less focused on Frankenstein's family in Geneva because the monster lacks that information.
- The murders of Clerval and Elizabeth might be presented less savagely and more like unfortunate necessities.
- The reader might learn more about how and why the monster led Frankenstein to the Arctic at the novel's end.

Pages 36-37: Symbolism, Imagery and Setting
1. The fire's warmth brings the monster "delight", suggesting that knowledge is helpful and good. However, when he touches it he is burned and lets out "a cry of pain", which shows that knowledge can also be harmful.
2. E.g. It symbolises Frankenstein. The tree is destroyed by "dazzling" lightning. This mirrors the "brilliant" light of Frankenstein's discovery which ultimately destroys him too.
3. a) E.g. "bright and joyous in his young beauty".
   b) E.g. "vivid flashes of lightning dazzled my eyes".
4. a) E.g. Frankenstein does most of his work at night.
   b) E.g. The monster can't make sense of his dark surroundings.
5. You should have ticked the first and second boxes.
6. E.g. At first, Frankenstein enjoys the "kindly influence" of nature. He then starts finding nature more difficult to enjoy until, eventually, he can't enjoy his surroundings at all.
7. E.g. "maternal Nature bade me weep no more."
E.g. Describing nature as "maternal" suggests it is caring, implying that nature nurtures and restores Frankenstein.
8. Walton's, Arctic, danger, Frankenstein's, loneliness, tension
9. E.g. Overnight Frankenstein's mood changes from being "at peace" to feeling a "dark melancholy". This is reflected by the rain "pouring in torrents" when he wakes up. The "thick mists" also mirror the way his thoughts are now "clouded".

Answers

Page 38: The Gothic Novel

1. a) E.g. Frankenstein makes a monster from body parts.
   b) E.g. Walton relays the story while travelling in the Arctic.
   c) E.g. The monster is made to feel cast out from society.
2. a) E.g. Frankenstein feels invisible "spirits" flying around his head, which seems oppressive and frightening.
   b) E.g. Frankenstein is "hurried away by fury", which suggests that more destruction is likely.
   c) E.g. Frankenstein is alone in the graveyard where his family are buried. This morbid setting reminds the reader of their deaths.
3. E.g. It encourages the reader to draw parallels between Frankenstein and the monster. This disturbs the reader by implying that little separates humans from monsters.

Page 39: Language

1. a) E.g. "heart-sickening despair"
   b) E.g. "Abhorred monster! Fiend that thou art!"
2. senses, memories, metaphor, revenge, burning
3. E.g. In his early letters he is optimistic and has faith in the "resolved will of man". However, his later letters have a dejected tone, as he has lost his "hopes of utility and glory".
4. E.g. The monster uses specific examples of abuse such as "spurned", "kicked" and "trampled" to show that he is a victim. He then uses rhetorical questions to get Walton to consider different points of view.

Exam Practice:

Your answer should have an introduction, several paragraphs developing different ideas and a conclusion. You may have included some of the following points:

- Shelley uses superlatives in this extract to emphasise Frankenstein's despair. He describes himself as "destined to become the most wretched" of humans. This emphasises the extreme nature of his grief by suggesting it will exceed that of all other people. Frankenstein's retrospective narration also means that this superlative foreshadows further heartbreak, as at this point in the novel he has 'only' lost a brother.
- Shelley suggests that Frankenstein's emotions are moved by nature. His emotions are linked to the weather in Chapter Nine when he is comforted by the wind, which "whispered in soothing accents" to him. This shows how his emotions are often positively influenced by the weather, suggesting that it has a healing effect on him. This presentation of the weather reflects the 'Romantic' idea that nature had the power to restore people's spirits.
- Shelley frequently uses similes to associate Frankenstein's feelings with powerful physical forces. His desire to create life is "like a hurricane" and his passion is "like a mountain river". The word "hurricane" suggests a mighty and destructive force that Frankenstein is powerless to stop, which emphasises the strength of his desire. This image also suggests that Frankenstein tries to avoid feeling the guilt his immoral actions inspire, as he is blaming his behaviour on powerful forces outside his control.

Page 40: Skills Focus — Working with Extracts

1. The extract is from early in Chapter 20. Frankenstein has been making a female creature in a laboratory. The monster is about to threaten to be at Frankenstein's wedding night.
2. E.g. It suggests that his emotions are overwhelming. He feels them so powerfully that he starts to shake.
3. E.g. The monster howls, which suggests he is wild and savage. It also implies his misery makes him less civilised.
4. E.g. In Chapter 4, "Winter, spring, and summer" pass while he works on the monster with little human contact.

Page 41: Practice Questions

Your answers should have an introduction, several paragraphs developing different ideas and a conclusion. You may have covered some of the following points:

1.
   - Shelley presents revenge as self-destructive in the extract. When the monster says his desire for revenge has made him "like the arch-fiend", he is comparing himself to Satan in Milton's poem, *Paradise Lost*. This simile suggests his desire for revenge has destroyed his good nature, as he likens himself to the Devil. This idea is reinforced in the extract by the way he describes "a hell" inside himself, which contrasts with the "good dispositions" he describes himself having in Chapter Fifteen.
   - Shelley creates a close link between revenge and the monster's destructive behaviour in this extract. He vows to get revenge on Frankenstein and mankind by declaring "everlasting war" on them. This image of his revenge as a battle underlines its damaging nature, and "everlasting" suggests the harm it causes will be endless. This is reflected in the rest of the novel, as the monster's thirst for revenge continues to cause death and destruction until the monster's own death.
   - Shelley shows how destructive Frankenstein's vengeful pursuit of the monster is. In Letter Four, Frankenstein is described as a "wrecked" ship and the tragedy he has suffered is presented as a "storm". This extended metaphor emphasises how Frankenstein's hunt for the monster swept his life off-course and led him to ruin. Later in the novel it becomes apparent that Frankenstein and the monster are locked in a vicious cycle of revenge, with each seeking to punish the other for past wrongs. This emphasises how long-lasting and destructive revenge can be.

2.
   - Shelley uses pathetic fallacy to create tension at the start of this extract. For example, Frankenstein says that the wind "rose with great violence". This pathetic fallacy makes the weather seem aggressive, which creates an ominous mood and reflects Frankenstein's unease. It also reminds the reader of the monster's violent threat, which builds a sense of impending danger. Representing emotions through nature was a common feature of 'Romantic' literature in the 19th century. Shelley uses this feature often in *Frankenstein* to build tension before sinister events.
   - Shelley also uses descriptive language to create tension in this extract. When Frankenstein hears Elizabeth's scream, he says that "every muscle and fibre was suspended" and refers to a "tingling" in his veins. The vivid description immerses the reader in the physical sensations Frankenstein feels, emphasising his fear. It also slows the pace of the narrative, holding it back at a time when the reader urgently wants to know what happens next. The reader's tension here is linked to Elizabeth's unknown fate. When her death is revealed, the tension is released and replaced with horror.
   - The structure of the novel leading up to this extract also helps to create tension. After the monster has threatened Frankenstein's "wedding-night" in Chapter Twenty, Frankenstein doesn't mention the threat again until referring to it three times in Chapter Twenty-Two. The way the threat resurfaces several times in this part of the narrative creates tension by drawing the reader's attention back to the monster's plan right before the wedding night. Shelley also begins to build tension about Elizabeth's fate earlier in the novel, when Frankenstein's dream of Elizabeth transforming into his dead mother in Chapter Five foreshadows Elizabeth's death.

Answers

3. • In the extract, Shelley uses the monster to show how companionship is necessary for people to be happy. The monster desires "a creature of another sex" to be "cut off from all the world" with him. This shows that he can accept being exiled as long as he is not alone, emphasising the importance of companionship to his well-being. This idea about companionship links to those of the 19th-century philosopher Rousseau, who explored how isolation could have a negative effect on someone in society. Shelley uses the monster's relationships with others in the novel to explore this idea.

 • Shelley presents companionship as important for Frankenstein's health. He becomes "happy" when he is with Clerval in Chapter Six, and is "calmed" by his father in Chapter Twenty-One. On the other hand, when Frankenstein is alone, he tends to become depressed and obsessive, which emphasises how crucial company is for ensuring his stability. This idea heightens the sense of tragedy when his companions die, as the reader can begin to anticipate Frankenstein's downfall.

 • Shelley shows how important companionship is to Walton. In his letters, he admits to his sister that he bitterly feels "the want of a friend". This explains why he forms an attachment to Frankenstein so quickly, and emphasises how valuable companionship is to him. The fact that the entire novel is made up of Walton's personal correspondence with his sister further highlights his need to feel connected to someone. His desire to share his experiences with a family member provides the epistolary frame which holds the rest of the novel in place.

4. a) • The language in this extract links the natural world with death and loss. The trees "lie broken and strewed" and the mist curls in "thick wreaths". The phrase "broken and strewed" evokes images of death and destruction, and the word "wreaths" reminds the reader of funerals. Uniting Frankenstein's powerful grief with these images of nature emphasises the overwhelming sense of loss in the extract. The morbid tone also creates a sinister atmosphere for the arrival of the monster later in the chapter.

 • The structure of this extract shows how Frankenstein's relationship with the natural world has changed since the start of the novel. In the first paragraph he reminisces about the "sublime ecstasy" he experienced the first time he saw the glacier, whereas in the second paragraph he notices the "melancholy impression" his surroundings give him now. Placing these two different perspectives so close together emphasises how the restorative effect nature used to have on Frankenstein has been lost. The fact that this change occurs after Frankenstein makes the monster suggests that his unnatural experiments corrupted his connection to the natural world.

 • The natural world is presented as isolated in this extract. Frankenstein travels alone and reaches a "scene terrifically desolate". This description makes the natural world sound bleak and empty by emphasising the solitude surrounding Frankenstein. The desolation reflects Frankenstein's mood in this extract because he cannot share his guilt with anyone, which makes him feel alone.

 b) • Clerval's response to his surroundings in Chapter Eighteen shows the positive impact that a setting can have on a character's mood. Clerval feels "a happiness seldom tasted by man" while taking in the wonderful scenery as he and Frankenstein travel through Europe. The extreme nature of his delight shows how powerful an effect his surroundings have upon him. Shelley uses Clerval's joy to demonstrate the 'Romantic' idea that nature is a powerful force which can inspire people.

 • Shelley uses the setting in 'Walton, in continuation' to show how surroundings can make characters feel threatened. When Walton's ship is stuck in the ice he feels "surrounded by mountains" that "admit of no escape". The words "surrounded" and "no escape" make his situation sound threatening and oppressive. This pessimistic response contrasts with Walton's earlier optimism, suggesting that bleak surroundings can influence the mood of even the most resolute characters.

 • Shelley presents the valley of Chamounix as having a healing effect on Victor. As he travels in Chapter Nine, he says the "weight" on his spirit "was sensibly lightened". The imagery of a heavy "weight" being lifted from Frankenstein's spirit emphasises how strong the valley's restorative power is. This suggests that the valley is a spiritual and almost religious force, as it revives Frankenstein's soul.

Section Five — Exam Buster

Page 42: Understanding the Question

1. b) <u>Explain how</u> the theme of <u>revenge</u> is <u>presented</u> in *Frankenstein*.
 c) <u>Explain how</u> <u>Frankenstein</u> <u>changes</u> <u>throughout</u> the novel.
 d) <u>How</u> is the theme of <u>ambition</u> <u>presented</u> in *Frankenstein*?
 e) <u>Explore</u> the <u>importance</u> of <u>family</u> in *Frankenstein*.
 f) <u>Write about</u> <u>how</u> <u>Caroline's</u> <u>goodness</u> is <u>presented</u> in *Frankenstein*.
 g) <u>How</u> does Shelley <u>create</u> an <u>atmosphere</u> of <u>horror</u> in the novel?

2. a - 4, b - 5, c - 1, d - 3, e - 2

Page 43: Making a Rough Plan

1. E.g. The monster shows a sophisticated understanding of human behaviour. / The monster enjoys reading and learning from books. / The monster learns the De Laceys' language faster than Safie.

2. Pick your three most important points and put them in a sensible order. Write down a quote or an example from the text to back up each one.

Page 44: Making Links

1. People are shown to be prejudiced. E.g. Safie's father was punished more severely by the French government because of his religion.
 People can be selfless. E.g. Caroline sacrifices her own life to nurse Elizabeth back to health.
 People need companionship and love. E.g. Walton describes having "no friend" with him as a "severe evil."

2. E.g. If one of your points was 'The monster enjoys reading and learning from books', and your evidence was that they gave him "extreme delight" when he finds them, another example could be that he pays "close attention" to Safie's French lessons so he could "more speedily master the language".

Page 45: Structuring Your Answer

1. Point: Frankenstein is taken over by his desire to get revenge on the monster.
 Example: This is shown when he tells Walton that his "vengeance" is "like a mighty tide".
 Explanation: The word "mighty" shows that Frankenstein's desire for revenge is extremely strong. The way the simile compares it to a powerful natural occurrence also implies that it is unstoppable.

Answers

Develop: By showing the extent of Frankenstein's fury, Shelley gives the reader a better understanding of why he pursues the monster so far for so long.

2. a) E.g. The monster planned to "reason" with Frankenstein.
   b) E.g. Frankenstein feels "melancholy" on his journey home.
3. Point: The monster enjoys reading and learning from books. Example: He describes the books he finds as "treasures" which bring him "delight".
   Explanation: The word "treasures" implies that the monster finds the books valuable, and "delight" emphasises the great pleasure he gets from reading them.
   Develop: By emphasising the value of the books, Shelley presents education as important. This idea is reinforced elsewhere in the novel, as the monster's ability to argue intelligently is partly what convinces Frankenstein to listen to him.

Page 46: Introductions and Conclusions

1. Intro b) is better, e.g. Intro a) focuses on a specific example and begins to analyse it. It is more like a P.E.E.D. paragraph than an introduction. Intro b) sets out several main points that can be explored later in the answer.
2. E.g. The conclusion should focus on how Shelley presents the monster as deserving of sympathy, rather than on how his presentation changes throughout the novel. It should also stay focused on answering the question, rather than introducing new evidence.
Task: Your introduction and conclusion should both give a clear answer to the question. The introduction should include your main points, but no evidence. Your conclusion should summarise your argument and not include new points.

Page 47: Writing about Context

1. a - 2, b - 1, c - 3
2. You should have underlined: "the novel's alternative title, 'The Modern Prometheus', which is inspired by Greek and Roman mythology. In the myth, Prometheus steals fire from the gods to give it to humans despite the gods forbidding him to do so."
3. You could have included context as the Explain or Develop part of the paragraph. The context you wrote about should be relevant to your Point and linked to the Example.

Page 48: Linking Ideas and Paragraphs

1. E.g. Shelley presents Henry Clerval in an idealised way to the reader. For example, he is described as being "perfectly humane" and "full of kindness" during Chapter 2. This creates a contrast between Clerval and Frankenstein, whose selfishness becomes more apparent as the novel goes on, and emphasises Clerval's virtue as a result. Because Shelley presents Clerval so virtuously, his murder is more shocking for the reader.
2. You should have used the P.E.E.D. structure and included connecting words and phrases such as 'therefore' or 'which shows that' to link your ideas.
3. E.g. Shelley also presents the monster as intelligent when... / This idea is reinforced by...

Page 49: Marking Answer Extracts

1. 4-5: E.g. The answer gives a thoughtful personal response to the text and integrates an appropriate example. It also examines how Shelley uses language to create meaning. However, the analysis of language isn't thorough enough to be a 6-7 answer, and there is no exploration of context. The range of sentence types is also only moderate, which helps to identify it as a 4-5 response.

Page 50: Marking Answer Extracts

1. a) 6-7: E.g. "Frankenstein's love for Elizabeth is made clear... allows Shelley to show their mutual love to the reader" — thorough exploration of form to create meaning. "Challenging her parents in this way... at the time the novel is set" — explores the relationship between the text and its context.
   b) 8-9: E.g. "Frankenstein and Elizabeth's relationship... what a poor match they are for each other" — insightful and critical personal response to the text. "This turning point shows that... main link to goodness and self-control" — highly relevant subject terminology.

Pages 51-52: Marking a Whole Answer

1. 8-9: E.g. The answer explores several different ways that Frankenstein is presented as ambitious. It engages with the text critically and insightfully, analysing how language, form and structure create meaning. There is also a detailed exploration of context and a wide variety of sentence types.

Page 53: Skills Focus — Writing Well

1. In the novel, Frankensteins' [Frankenstein's] monster is described as being different too [to] mankind. He says he can endure more extreme temperatures with "less injury' ["] to himself, and that he can "subsist upon coarser diet" than humans can. Ultimately, these differences caused [cause] him disstress [distress], as they make him feel "deformed" and alone, [.]
2. You could have rewritten the sentences as follows:
   a) The monster is good-natured at first, but he is abused by everyone he meets which makes him behave immorally.
   b) Frankenstein struggles to cope with the horrific things he experiences throughout the novel.
   c) Justine's execution shows the reader how prejudiced society can be.
   d) Shelley frequently highlights the dangers of obsession in the novel to show how destructive it can be.

Page 54: Practice Questions

Your answers should have an introduction, several paragraphs developing different ideas and a conclusion. You might have covered some of the following points:

1. • Embedded letters are used to give the reader extra information. In this extract, Elizabeth's letter shows her "apprehensions" about Frankenstein's illness and her desire for him to return to Geneva. This gives the reader a more direct insight into her feelings, which they would normally have to infer from Frankenstein's own thoughts. In this way, embedded letters also allow Shelley to add more depth to characters. Elizabeth wishes to visit Frankenstein but says she isn't "able" to, which reveals the expectation placed on her to stay and care for the family as the only female figure left in it.
   • Letters encourage the reader to engage with the characters more closely. Frankenstein's epistolary form means the reader hears from many of the novel's main characters in the first person. This makes it easier for the reader to engage with key characters like Frankenstein and Walton, as they feel as though they are being directly addressed by them. Including multiple first-person narratives also encourages the reader to draw more detailed comparisons between characters, as they have access to their different thoughts.
   • Letters highlight Walton's unreliability as a narrator. In 'Walton, in continuation', Walton heaps praise upon Frankenstein, calling him "noble and godlike". His

Answers

description to his sister implies that Frankenstein is holy by linking him to virtue and God. The implication that Frankenstein is worthy of being worshipped reveals Walton's tendency to exaggerate Frankenstein's goodness in his letters. This is particularly evident to the reader at this point in the novel, as the full extent of Frankenstein's wrongdoing has been revealed in the narrative.

2. a) • In this extract, Shelley presents society reacting to the monster with fear. The shepherd and children "shrieked" when they saw the monster, and a woman "fainted". Shelley's presentation of everyone, from men and women to children, reacting to the monster with fear implies that all of humanity is afraid of him. Just after this in the text, the monster references Milton's 1667 poem *Paradise Lost* by comparing his hut to "Pandæmonium" (the capital of Hell) where "the dæmons of hell" find refuge. This reference could imply that the monster is subconsciously becoming more like the fearful being society sees him as.

   • Shelley presents society's response to the monster as aggressive. The words "attacked", "missile" and "weapons" are used to describe the villagers' response to him. This creates an image of battle, which suggests that the villagers band together like an army and view the monster as their enemy. It also highlights their instinctive desire to attack him. Despite society reacting so violently towards the monster, he doesn't attack anyone in response, which emphasises to the reader that the villagers' aggression is unfounded.

   • Shelley suggests that society misunderstands the monster in the extract. The monster's experience of being "enchanted" by the shepherd's hut and the "miraculous" village is lost on the villagers, who only want to fight him or flee from him. Contrasting the monster's innocent curiosity with the villagers' instant rejection of him demonstrates how society misinterprets the monster's intentions based solely on his appearance. Ironically, it is this prejudice which ultimately causes the monster to become the evil and fearful creature that the villagers already see him as.

   b) • Prejudice is shown to be deeply ingrained in society. As well as being attacked by the villagers, the monster is rejected by the De Laceys in Chapter Fifteen, then shot by a "rustic" and called "an ogre" by William in Chapter Sixteen. By showing prejudiced behaviour recurring in a wide range of characters and social classes, Shelley shows how this behaviour is deeply embedded in society. This idea is supported in the rest of the novel, as the monster isn't the only character to experience prejudice.

   • Shelley presents prejudice as irrational in the novel. While Frankenstein creates the monster, he refers to it as his "child", but once his work is finished he immediately views the monster as a "wretch" who causes "disgust". His change in attitude from the positive connotations of "child" to the negative ones of "wretch" is sudden, which makes his reaction seem rash and erratic. This encourages the reader to see his prejudice against the monster as illogical. The fact that the monster's own creator becomes prejudiced against him also shows how powerful prejudice can be, in spite of its absurdity.

   • Shelley shows that prejudice can be inspired by fear and jealousy. The French courts are shown to be prejudiced against Safie's father in Chapter Fourteen, as the reader learns that his "religion and wealth" cause the court to punish him more severely. This implies that the court treated him unjustly because it felt threatened by his prosperity and identity as an 'outsider'. A 19th-century reader might have related to this prejudice more easily, as Britain was much less multicultural at the time when Shelley was writing, and many people feared 'outsiders'.

3. • In the extract, Shelley presents friendship positively. Frankenstein's "delight" upon seeing Clerval dismisses his "horror and misfortune". This suggests his friendship with Clerval brings him happiness. The opposition Shelley creates in Frankenstein's transformation from "horror" to "delight" also implies that Clerval's positive influence is extremely powerful. This idea is emphasised towards the end of the novel, when Frankenstein can still recall the sound of Clerval's voice after Clerval has died.

   • In the novel, Shelley uses Clerval to show that friendship is an important source of love. Later in Chapter Five, Clerval delays his education to be Frankenstein's "nurse", in Chapter Seven he offers comforting words of "heartfelt sympathy" and in Chapter Nineteen he says he cannot feel "at home" without Frankenstein. His consistent care shows the extent to which love is displayed in friendship. Because the novel is set in a patriarchal 19th-century society, the importance of loving male friendships is emphasised, as many men like Clerval would not have socialised closely with women until marriage.

   • Friendship is also presented as a source of hardship. In Chapter Twenty-Four, Frankenstein says his "rage choked" him when he was grieving his friends. The image that Frankenstein is so furious his body is unable to work normally highlights the pain the loss of his friends causes him. The monster demonstrates a similar tortured reaction when he is overwhelmed by a "rage of anger" after the De Laceys reject him. This further highlights the parallel between Frankenstein and the monster to the reader, as they both experience anger when friendships, whether they are real or wished for, end suddenly.

4. • Frankenstein's grief causes him to suffer in the extract. He describes a "weight" which "pressed" on him, and being "seized by remorse". Frankenstein highlights his discomfort to Walton with the verbs "seized" and "pressed", which imply that he was being tightly bound in place. This suggests he felt he could not escape his misery. The fact that he is the object of each verb also emphasises the idea that he is a victim, as he presents himself as having something done to him. However, a lot of the language used to describe Frankenstein's suffering in the extract is hyperbolic. Shelley may therefore be implying that his suffering is exaggerated.

   • Shelley shows that Frankenstein is victimised by the monster. Towards the end of the novel, the monster develops an "insatiable thirst for vengeance" when he discovers Frankenstein plans to marry Elizabeth. The word "insatiable" implies that the monster's desire for revenge is unstoppable, which shows how powerless Frankenstein is to prevent Elizabeth's murder. This lack of power highlights Frankenstein's vulnerability and emphasises how he is at the mercy of the monster.

   • On the other hand, Frankenstein is also presented as deserving of his misery. Shelley says that he "dabbled" in graves and "tortured" animals while they were still alive. This immoral behaviour demonstrates how little respect Frankenstein shows to others, which creates a sense of hypocrisy when he feels victimised for being wronged. Furthermore, as Frankenstein assumes the role of a God-like creator by making his own "new species", his later suffering may have been viewed by 19th-century readers as a fitting punishment from God.

The Characters in 'Frankenstein'

Phew! You should be an expert on *Frankenstein* by now. But if you want a bit of light relief and a quick recap of the novel's plot, sit yourself down and read through Frankenstein — The Cartoon...

Victor
Frankenstein

As a child

Monster

Robert
Walton

Elizabeth
Lavenza

As a child

Henry
Clerval

Alphonse
Frankenstein

Justine Moritz

Mary Shelley's 'Frankenstein'

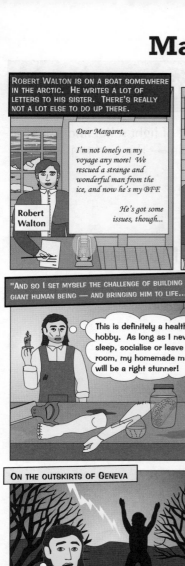

ROBERT WALTON IS ON A BOAT SOMEWHERE IN THE ARCTIC. HE WRITES A LOT OF LETTERS TO HIS SISTER. THERE'S REALLY NOT A LOT ELSE TO DO UP THERE.

Dear Margaret,

I'm not lonely on my voyage any more! We rescued a strange and wonderful man from the ice, and now he's my BFF.

He's got some issues, though...

Robert Walton

I'm on this cold and dangerous journey to discover the secrets of the North Pole. I won't allow myself to fail — I want to change the world!

Wait! Before you let your ambition destroy you, listen to my long and detailed tale of woe...

Victor Frankenstein

"I WAS BORN AND RAISED IN GENEVA. WHEN I WAS FIVE, MY BELOVED PARENTS ADOPTED A YOUNG GIRL NAMED ELIZABETH. SHE SOON BECAME MY CLOSEST FRIEND."

Victor, we've got you a present — a new sister!

And she'll make you a cracking wife one day!

Caroline (Victor's Mother)

Er, thanks?

Alphonse (Victor's Father)

Victor

Elizabeth

"MY PARENTS HAD TWO MORE SONS, ERNEST AND WILLIAM. BUT WHEN I WAS 17, OUR MOTHER FELL ILL AND DIED. SOON AFTERWARDS, I LEFT HOME TO GO TO UNIVERSITY IN INGOLSTADT."

For the ambitious modern scientist, anything is possible!

Ping

science science science
science science scien
science science scien
science science s

Anything? That gives me an idea...

Prof Waldman

"AND SO I SET MYSELF THE CHALLENGE OF BUILDING A GIANT HUMAN BEING — AND BRINGING HIM TO LIFE..."

This is definitely a healthy hobby. As long as I never sleep, socialise or leave my room, my homemade man will be a right stunner!

MONTHS OF HARD TOIL LATER...

Blauugh...

Frankenstein's Monster

Argh, my beautiful superman is alive — and he's a horrific monster! What was I thinking? Time to run away and have a nervous breakdown.

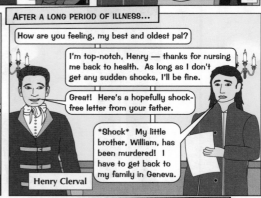

AFTER A LONG PERIOD OF ILLNESS...

How are you feeling, my best and oldest pal?

I'm top-notch, Henry — thanks for nursing me back to health. As long as I don't get any sudden shocks, I'll be fine.

Great! Here's a hopefully shock-free letter from your father.

Shock My little brother, William, has been murdered! I have to get back to my family in Geneva.

Henry Clerval

ON THE OUTSKIRTS OF GENEVA

I'd recognise that hideous eight-foot-tall silhouette anywhere — it's my monster. If he's here, I'll bet he murdered William... and it's probably all my fault!

JUSTINE, THE FRANKENSTEINS' MAID, IS ACCUSED OF WILLIAM'S MURDER

Justine Moritz, the court finds you guilty of murdering William Frankenstein — and stealing his golden locket. We sentence you to death.

Gasp

Justine was our servant, but she was like a sister to me, too. I'll always believe she's innocent.

Justine

Elizabeth

She is innocent! But if I try to explain, they'll all think I've lost my mind. I'd better run away again.

JUSTINE IS EXECUTED, AND VICTOR GOES WANDERING

Ah, fresh mountain air. Much better than facing up to my responsibilities.

Aw, not you again... I'll kill you! Prepare to meet your maker!

Wait! Before you try to destroy me, listen to my long and detailed tale of woe...

"I WAS A KIND, GENTLE, INNOCENT CREATURE. BUT I SOON LEARNED THAT HUMANS DIDN'T LIKE THE LOOK OF ME."

Eat brick, ugly beast!

Hwagh!

"SO I HID IN AN OLD HOVEL NEXT TO A COTTAGE. MY NEW NEIGHBOURS WERE THE DE LACEY FAMILY."

"BY WATCHING THEM, I LEARNED TO SPEAK, TO READ... AND TO LOVE."

Tree... flower... husband... happiness...

You're doing a great job of learning our language, Safie.

Agatha

De Lacey

Felix

Yes, even I can see that (and I'm blind, FYI).

Safie

"I DESPERATELY WANTED TO BE LOVED AND ACCEPTED BY THE DE LACEYS. I DECIDED TO START WITH THE BLIND OLD MAN — HE WOULDN'T JUDGE ME ON MY LOOKS."

Hello, sir — I'm a COMPLETELY NORMAL PERSON who definitely hasn't been spying on you for months.

Welcome! You sound like a nice tall chap.

"BUT THE OTHERS WEREN'T KEEN ON ME."

Oh, hi. Anyone fancy a game of Happy Families?

Get away from us, you... thing!

Eek!

"I HATED MYSELF — AND I HATED YOU EVEN MORE. YOU'D CREATED ME AS A MONSTER, THEN LEFT ME TO FEND FOR MYSELF. SO I WENT TO GENEVA, LOOKING FOR REVENGE. THAT'S WHEN I MET YOUR BROTHER, WILLIAM... AND KILLED HIM."

William

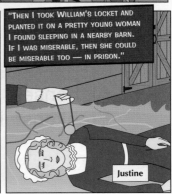

"THEN I TOOK WILLIAM'S LOCKET AND PLANTED IT ON A PRETTY YOUNG WOMAN I FOUND SLEEPING IN A NEARBY BARN. IF I WAS MISERABLE, THEN SHE COULD BE MISERABLE TOO — IN PRISON."

Justine